Healing Spaces

Healing Spaces

Designing Physical Environments to Optimize Health, Wellbeing and Performance

Special Issue Editors

Altaf Engineer
Esther M. Sternberg
Aletheia Ida

MDPI • Basel • Beijing • Wuhan • Barcelona • Belgrade • Manchester • Tokyo • Cluj • Tianjin

Special Issue Editors

Altaf Engineer
University of Arizona
USA

Esther M. Sternberg
University of Arizona
USA

Aletheia Ida
University of Arizona
USA

Editorial Office
MDPI
St. Alban-Anlage 66
4052 Basel, Switzerland

This is a reprint of articles from the Special Issue published online in the open access journal *International Journal of Environmental Research and Public Health* (ISSN 1660-4601) (available at: https://www.mdpi.com/journal/ijerph/special_issues/healing_spaces).

For citation purposes, cite each article independently as indicated on the article page online and as indicated below:

LastName, A.A.; LastName, B.B.; LastName, C.C. Article Title. *Journal Name* **Year**, *Article Number, Page Range*.

ISBN 978-3-03936-376-6 (Hbk)
ISBN 978-3-03936-377-3 (PDF)

Cover image courtesy of Esther M. Sternberg.

Contents

About the Special Issue Editors

Altaf Engineer, PhD, is an assistant professor at the School of Architecture and University of Arizona Institute on Place, Wellbeing and Performance (UA IPWP), an interdisciplinary institute at the University of Arizona that links together the expertise of the UA College of Medicine, Tucson, the Arizona Center for Integrative Medicine (AzCIM), and the UA College of Architecture, Planning and Landscape Architecture (CAPLA). He is also Chair of the Master of Science in Architecture—Health and Built Environment Program (MS Arch—HBE). Dr. Engineer completed a PhD in Architecture and a Master of Architecture at the University of Illinois at Urbana-Champaign, where he was an Illinois Distinguished Fellow for three years and was awarded the ARCC King's Merit Medal for Excellence in Architectural + Environmental Behavior Research. He earned his Bachelor of Architecture from the University of Mumbai, India. He is a registered architect in New York, USA. He is also a LEED Accredited Professional, with ten plus years of experience in sustainable higher education buildings, institutional buildings, adaptive re-use and residential projects. Dr. Engineer received the 2018 Emerging Legacy Award from the College of Fine and Applied Arts, University of Illinois at Urbana-Champaign. This award recognizes alumni and friends who have demonstrated courage, curiosity and passion in their work, and honors individuals who have impacted their fields in transformative ways—catalysts with a distinguished service to the arts. Dr. Engineer was nominated and selected after an internal review by a committee of representatives from across the University of Illinois FAA college, community and administration. Dr. Engineer's scholarship, teaching and practice are informed by his interest in social, cultural and behavioral factors in design, with a special focus on daylighting, health and wellbeing. He is the first author of the book Shedding New Light On Art Museum Additions: Front Stage and Back Stage Experiences, published in 2018.

Esther M. Sternberg, MD, is a professor of medicine and the Andrew Weil Chair for Research in Integrative Medicine at the University of Arizona College of Medicine, Tucson. She is also the Research Director of the Andrew Weil Center for Integrative Medicine and the Director of the UArizona Institute on Place, Wellbeing & Performance. A native of Canada, Dr. Sternberg earned her bachelor's degree and medical doctorate from McGill University in Quebec, Canada, in 1972 and 1974, respectively. She completed both her residency in internal medicine and her fellowship in rheumatology at McGill University. Internationally recognized for her discoveries in the science of the mind–body interaction in illness and healing, Dr. Sternberg is a major force in collaborative initiatives on mind–body–stress–wellness and environment interrelationships. Her best-selling popular books, Healing Spaces: The Science of Place and Well-Being and The Balance Within: The Science Connecting Health and Emotions, are informative and scientifically based, and inspire doctors and lay persons alike to deal with the complexities and 21st century frontiers of stress, healing and wellness. Dr. Sternberg's many honors include recognition by the National Library of Medicine as one of 300 women physicians who have changed the face of medicine, the Anita Roberts National Institutes of Health Distinguished Woman Scientist Lectureship, and an honorary doctorate in medicine from Trinity College, Dublin. Currently working as Research Director of the Andrew Weil Center for Integrative Medicine, University of Arizona, Tucson, Dr. Sternberg was previously Section Chief of Neuroendocrine Immunology and Behavior at the National Institute of Mental Health; Director of the Integrative Neural Immune Program, NIMH/NIH; and Co-Chair of the NIH Intramural Program on Research on Women's Health. She has been featured in numerous radio and television programs, including PBS's The New Medicine and Life Part II, NPR's Speaking of Faith and, in 2009, with Emmy Award-winning Resolution Pictures, created and hosted a PBS special based on her books: The Science of Healing. Well known for her ability to translate complex scientific subjects for lay audiences, Sternberg has testified before Congress, advised the World Health Organization, and is a regular contributor to Science Magazine's "Books et al." column. She is also a regular columnist for Arthritis Today. A dynamic speaker, recognized by her peers as a spokesperson for the field, Sternberg translates complex scientific subjects in a highly accessible manner, with a combination of academic credibility, passion for science and compassion as a physician. Dr. Sternberg lectures nationally and internationally to both lay and scientific audiences and is frequently interviewed on radio, television and film and in print media, on subjects including the mind–body connection, 'stress and illness', spirituality, love, and health, and place and well-being. She is a member of the University of Arizona Arthritis Center Scientific Advisory Council and was the keynote presenter at the 2013 University of Arizona Living Healthy With Arthritis Conference.

Aletheia Ida, PhD, is an architect and assistant professor at the School of Architecture. She teaches courses in design studio, research methods, environmentally adaptive systems, emerging materials, building enclosures, environmental building technology design theory, as well as independent research and thesis advising. Aletheia earned her accredited Bachelor of Architecture degree from the University of Oregon, post-professional Master of Architecture in Design and Energy Conservation from the University of Arizona, and Doctorate in Architectural Sciences from the Center for Architecture, Science and Ecology at the Rensselaer Polytechnic Institute. She integrates design theory into her research, for emergent environmental building technologies and incorporating aspects of material inventions with socio-environmental performance criteria through innovative digital and physical prototyping methods. She holds a provisional co-patent for Building Integrated Biopolymer Sorption Systems and a National Science Foundation EAGER award.

International Journal of
Environmental Research and Public Health

Editorial

Healing Spaces: Designing Physical Environments to Optimize Health, Wellbeing, and Performance

Altaf Engineer [1,2], Aletheia Ida [1,2] and Esther M. Sternberg [2,3,*]

1   School of Architecture, University of Arizona, Tucson, AZ 85721, USA; aengineer@email.arizona.edu (A.E.); aida@email.arizona.edu (A.I.)
2   UArizona Institute on Place, Wellbeing & Performance, University of Arizona, Tucson, AZ 85711, USA
3   Andrew Weil Center for Integrative Medicine, University of Arizona, Tucson, AZ 85711, USA
*   Correspondence: esternberg@email.arizona.edu

Received: 3 February 2020; Accepted: 9 February 2020; Published: 12 February 2020

Abstract: This Special Issue on Healing Spaces includes eight articles consisting of studies at the interface between design and health. The articles address some of the latest findings using state-of-the-art technologies, important outcomes for human health and wellbeing, and suggest exciting directions for the future of this research field.

Keywords: human health; built environment; urban open space; forest healing; wellbeing; psychology; physiology

---

The field of design and health, previously the purview of healthcare design professionals, has reached a new turning point where health impacts are becoming a focal point for designing environments on all scales. Many factors, including economic and societal, have contributed to this trend, but a large contributor is the proliferation of non-invasive wearable and stationary technologies measuring both health and environmental factors, which provide objective evidence for the real-time impacts of the built environment on many aspects of health, wellbeing, and performance. Research conducted with emerging tools is allowing for the discovery of human health variables in correlation to built environment conditions in expansive new ways. Each paper in this edited collection utilizes such technologies, knowledge from medical science, and sophisticated data analytics to discover relationships between environments and human wellbeing.

This Special Issue of "Healing Spaces: Designing Physical Environments to Optimize Health, Wellbeing and Performance" in the *International Journal of Environmental Research and Public Health* (*IJERPH*) includes articles that address a spectrum of human health measures in different contexts. The techniques and methods vary, ranging from electroencephalography (EEG) devices to record frontal alpha symmetry (FAA) values, to correlational human subject surveys that assess mood states and other extrinsic and intrinsic human wellbeing factors. In some cases, the human subject research data is collected in real-time in the settings of interest, while in others the data is collected in a pre- and post-setting experience through laboratory testing. The settings and contexts tested also vary, ranging from urban public spaces to natural forests.

The eight articles published in this issue focus on objective outcomes for human health and wellbeing based on measurements, which in turn leads to implications for the design of built environments for better health and wellbeing. This Special Issue provides both foundational knowledge for an emerging field of research as well as specialized results for design application.

In the first paper, Olszewska-Guizzo et al. [1] discuss mental health outcomes from exposure to green spaces in urban areas. The authors test the accuracy of different methods for predicting positive mental health and wellbeing outcomes from urban landscape exposures. They also discuss the specific features of urban green spaces that may be most beneficial for mental health and wellbeing. The results of the study inform prevention and intervention measures for mental health, future research in the field, and design guidelines for optimal urban green spaces.

Lyu et al. [2] study how bamboo forest therapy impacts immune system responses and psychophysiology of male college students. While bamboo forest therapy is identified as a fast-growing form of stress management, there is a knowledge gap in its specific health benefits, as the authors indicate. Some of the important findings of their study include an increase in positive mood states along with a reduction in negative mood states, and a decrease in heart rate, blood pressure, and corticosterone levels in the male participants exposed to forest environments. The authors, conclude that a three-day bamboo forest therapy session improves immune function, and physiological and psychological well-being in their participant cohort. Importantly, they recommend further studies to evaluate impacts on cardiovascular disease, hypertension, and cancer.

Plans et al. [3] study the relationship between the density of green spaces and cardiovascular risk factors and whether this relationship is different for male and female residents in the city of Madrid, Spain. The cardiovascular risk factors studied include obesity, diabetes, hypertension, and high cholesterol. The findings reveal a moderate association between these risk factors, except for obesity, and the density of green spaces within different proximities (buffer sizes) for females, but not for males. More research on gender differences and their relationship to green spaces of different buffer sizes and cardiovascular health is therefore much-needed, as per the authors. The findings of this study, nonetheless, provide evidence for policy-makers wishing to create healthier environments in cities and reduce gender inequities.

Molina-García et al. [4] study the role of neighborhood characteristics in influencing physically active and sedentary behaviors in university students—a topic that has not been studied before, according to the authors. The authors find associations between neighborhood-built environments and socioeconomic status with active commuting, leisure-time physical activity, and sedentary behavior among university students. They discuss the implications of these findings, which include the design of university residential environments to promote walkability, available transportation, and exercise in college students.

Chien et al. [5] discuss the benefits of urban open spaces on human health. Specifically, they examine the associations between the proximity to open spaces and adult renal function. The results reveal that a lower prevalence of chronic kidney disease is associated with proximity to open space among adults in Taiwan without hypertension or impaired fasting glucose. This paper highlights the positive association between open spaces and human physiology and complements the first paper, which shows the positive relationship between green spaces and mental health in urban areas. Additionally, the findings hold much significance for countries with a high population density, such as Taiwan, since it makes a stronger case for more open spaces to improve the health of residents.

Takayama et al. [6] examine and compare the restorative effects of urban and forest settings on people. They find forest settings to have higher restorative properties than urban irrespective of individual traits, thereby highlighting the greater psychological and physiological benefits of forest environments. The authors call for more research on the relationship between forest settings and individual traits, and conclude by emphasizing the importance of developing forest experience programs suited for different individual trait types. The findings of this study highlight the effectiveness of forest therapy at combating daily stressors in urban life. As per the authors, this study could also be used to develop short-term forest staying programs for better psychological health in urban dwellers.

Shepley et al. [7] conduct an in-depth literature review to reveal the relationship between the presence of urban green spaces and the frequency of violent crime. Using a qualitative method, they find that green interventions in built urban environments, such as vegetated streets, walkways, community gardens, or simply the amount of tree cover, resulted in a reduction in crime. While the results for the relationship between city parks and undeveloped green areas and crime were inconclusive, the authors recommend more meta-analyses and qualitative studies on the topic so that city governments and communities may use the data to support more effective interventions to mitigate violent crime in urban settings.

Devos et al. [8], in the last paper of this Special Issue, emphasize the importance of acoustic environments to support persons with dementia. From a review of key concepts related to soundscapes, cognitive deficits, and other related behaviors, the authors propose a new framework for the composition and improvement of acoustic environments in dementia care environments. This framework consists of acoustic stimuli to influence moods, triggering feelings of safety, and other beneficial responses for residents with dementia. Optimal acoustic design for healthy spaces is often given less importance than visual or haptic design. This paper, therefore, makes an important contribution to the field.

Seven of the eight research studies focus on the urban and natural environments, using either open space or forest conditions as the spatial modality for human wellbeing impact. The eighth article is the only paper focusing on indoor memory care environments, though more specifically on the soundscape as an environment. Since papers were not targeted or solicited for this Special Issue in any particular domain, the preponderance of focus on urban and natural environments may reflect the well-established and long history of health studies at the urban planning scale, in contrast to the relatively recent advent of objective health measures at the individual building scale, beyond removing toxins from such environments. As the field of design and health continues to expand beyond healthcare facilities and public open space, we anticipate more human health research will emerge for varying indoor environments and programmatic uses. We envision that all spaces of the designed built environment, whether indoor, outdoor, urban, or natural, have the potential to contribute to human wellbeing and healing.

While each study reported here includes a relatively low number of participants, in combination, they provide increasing evidence for the health benefits of green spaces, whether urban or forest. The fact that these studies spanned the globe, from Spain, China, Taiwan, Singapore, to Japan and the US, is also indicative of the universal benefits of green spaces, regardless of culture or location. The articles in this special issue demonstrate how the built environment directly or indirectly affects human psychology, physiology, and overall wellbeing. We hope that this will stimulate more research in the burgeoning field of design and health. The interactions between humans and their environments are complex, and involve individual traits besides social, cultural, and behavioral issues. We are excited to see how more innovations in bio-sensing technology can help researchers address these issues to improve overall human health, wellbeing, and performance. As researchers continue to address knowledge gaps and take on new challenges, we look forward to mounting evidence for the health effects of built and natural environments at all scales and building types, impacting future directions in education, practice, and policy for the built environment.

Author Contributions: A.E., A.I., and E.M.S. collaboratively wrote and revised drafts of this editorial before finalizing. All authors have read and agreed to the published version of the manuscript.

Funding: This editorial work received no external funding.

Acknowledgments: The authors wish to acknowledge the work and contributions of IJERPH editors, staff, and all the scholarly reviewers who made this special issue possible.

Conflicts of Interest: The authors declare no conflict of interest.

References

1. Olszewska-Guizzo, A.; Sia, A.; Fogel, A.; Ho, R. Can exposure to certain urban green spaces trigger frontal alpha asymmetry in the brain?—Preliminary findings from a passive task EEG study. *Int. J. Environ. Res. Public Health* **2020**, *17*, 394. [CrossRef] [PubMed]
2. Lyu, B.; Zeng, C.; Xie, S.; Li, D.; Lin, W.; Li, N.; Jiang, M.; Liu, S.; Chen, Q. Benefits of a three-day bamboo forest therapy session on the psychophysiology and immune system responses of male college students. *Int. J. Environ. Res. Public Health* **2019**, *16*, 4991. [CrossRef] [PubMed]

3. Plans, E.; Gullón, P.; Cebrecos, A.; Fontán, M.; Díez, J.; Nieuwenhuijsen, M.; Franco, M. Density of green spaces and cardiovascular risk factors in the city of Madrid: The Heart Healthy Hoods Study. *Int. J. Environ. Res. Public Health* **2019**, *16*, 4918. [CrossRef] [PubMed]

4. Molina-García, J.; Menescardi, C.; Estevan, I.; Martínez-Bello, V.; Queralt, A. Neighborhood built environment and socioeconomic status are associated with active commuting and sedentary behavior, but not with leisure-time physical activity, in University students. *Int. J. Environ. Res. Public Health* **2019**, *16*, 3176. [CrossRef] [PubMed]

5. Chien, J.-W.; Yang, Y.-R.; Chen, S.-Y.; Chang, Y.-J.; Chan, C.-C. Urban open space is associated with better renal function of adult residents in New Taipei City. *Int. J. Environ. Res. Public Health* **2019**, *16*, 2436. [CrossRef] [PubMed]

6. Takayama, N.; Morikawa, T.; Bielinis, E. Relation between psychological restorativeness and lifestyle, quality of life, resilience, and stress-coping in forest settings. *Int. J. Environ. Res. Public Health* **2019**, *16*, 1456. [CrossRef] [PubMed]

7. Shepley, M.; Sachs, N.; Sadatsafavi, H.; Fournier, C.; Peditto, K. The impact of green space on violent crime in urban environments: An evidence synthesis. *Int. J. Environ. Res. Public Health* **2019**, *16*, 5119. [CrossRef] [PubMed]

8. Devos, P.; Aletta, F.; Thomas, P.; Petrovic, M.; Vander Mynsbrugge, T.; Van de Velde, D.; De Vriendt, P.; Botteldooren, D. Designing supportive soundscapes for nursing home residents with dementia. *Int. J. Environ. Res. Public Health* **2019**, *16*, 4904. [CrossRef] [PubMed]

International Journal of
*Environmental Research
and Public Health*

Concept Paper

Designing Supportive Soundscapes for Nursing Home Residents with Dementia

Paul Devos [1,*], Francesco Aletta [1,2], Pieter Thomas [1], Mirko Petrovic [3],
Tara Vander Mynsbrugge [4], Dominique Van de Velde [4,5], Patricia De Vriendt [4,5]
and Dick Botteldooren [1]

[1]   Department of Information Technology, Ghent University, 9052 Ghent, Belgium; f.aletta@ucl.ac.uk (F.A.);
      pieter.thomas@ugent.be (P.T.); Dick.Botteldooren@UGent.be (D.B.)
[2]   Institute for Environmental Design and Engineering, University College London, London WC1H0NN, UK
[3]   Department of Internal Medicine and Paediatrics, Ghent University, 9000 Ghent, Belgium;
      Mirko.Petrovic@UGent.be
[4]   Department of Occupational Therapy, Artevelde University College, 9000 Ghent, Belgium;
      tara.vandermynsbrugge@arteveldehs.be (T.V.M.); dominique.vandevelde@arteveldehs.be (D.V.d.V.);
      Patricia.DeVriendt@arteveldehs.be (P.D.V.)
[5]   Department of Occupational Therapy, Ghent University, 9000 Ghent, Belgium
*   Correspondence: p.devos@ugent.be

Received: 31 October 2019; Accepted: 28 November 2019; Published: 4 December 2019

Abstract: Sound and its resulting soundscape is a major appraisal component of the living environment. Where environmental sounds (e.g., outdoor traffic sounds) are often perceived as negative, a soundscape (e.g., containing natural sounds) can also have a positive effect on health and well-being. This supportive effect of a soundscape is getting increasing attention for use in practice. This paper addresses the design of a supportive sonic environment for persons with dementia in nursing homes. Starting from a review of key mechanisms related to sonic perception, cognitive deficits and related behavior, a framework is derived for the composition of a sonic environment for persons with dementia. The proposed framework is centered around using acoustic stimuli for influencing mood, stimulating the feeling of safety and triggering a response in a person. These stimuli are intended to be deployed as added sounds in a nursing home to improve the well-being and behavior of the residents.

Keywords: supportive soundscape; sonic environment; nursing homes; ageing; dementia

---

1. Introduction

As ageing is a dominant concern of today's society, adopting health care towards the needs of older people is an important challenge. With regard to ageing, one of the major causes of disability and dependency among older people is dementia. Dementia is a syndrome in which abnormal cognitive impairment leads to disability and dependency. It is the additional deterioration of cognitive capabilities compared to normal ageing deterioration. It originates from underlying disease induced brain changes and results in impairment of memory, thinking, orientation, awareness, comprehension, calculation, learning capacity, language and judgment [1]. As a consequence daily functioning is hindered. Dementia can also result in challenging behavior, leading to a variety of Behavioral and Psychological Symptoms of Dementia (BPSD). Different underlying diseases like prion disease, Alzheimer disease, vascular dementia, fronto-temporal dementia (e.g., semantic dementia), Parkinsons' disease, dementia with Lewy bodies and others are known to result in dementia, with 47 million people affected worldwide and a prevalence of 10 million affected people each year [2,3].

In order to have permanent care guaranteed from accessible and supportive care givers, people with dementia can reside in nursing homes. Such institutions are operating to provide residential accommodation with supervision from nursing staff 24 h a day, meals, help with personal care needs and additional specialized services to older people. The residents occupy a sleeping room and can reside during specific daytime periods in a living room, where social interaction and group support can take place. As the behavior of a person is related to his well-being, the underlying determinants like health, environment and social activity are important aspects for the delivery of a high quality of life in these accommodations. In order to guarantee a high quality of life for the residents and especially in the case of residents with dementia the provided care should span medical, social and supportive care [4].

There is a growing understanding of how various aspects of the living environment could affect health and well-being, in particular for persons with reduced mental capabilities. Directly, as well as indirectly, this also affects care professionals. Such understanding is needed in the design of healing environments [5].

An important component of the living environment is the sonic environment, which, in combination with the perception of it by a person or a group of persons in a specific context, is known as a soundscape. A sonic environment and a soundscape are related but they are not quite the same thing. The former refers to the collection of physical sounds present and audible in a given space, while the latter is the perceptual construct resulting for a person exposed to this sonic environment. The ISO working group recently clarified this issue by defining the soundscape as an "acoustic environment as perceived or experienced and/or understood by a person or people, in context" [6]. Thus, it is essential to understand what people actually "perceive" instead of merely measuring the physical properties of a sonic environment. The context considered here is a typical nursing home, which is a medicalized, institutional care and living facility context.

By providing people with signals about the environment they experience, sound plays a crucial role as it can influence cognition and thus, also behavior [7]. Many studies dealing with the treatment of persons with dementia were underpinned by sensory stimulation but often failed to properly consider the everyday sonic environment and its potential to influence persons either positively or negatively [8]. Nevertheless, the auditory domain should be carefully taken into account for persons with dementia, since they are likely to rely more on sound than other people, due to a high prevalence of visual impairments compared to hearing impairments [9]. For this group of people, indeed, sound is often the pathway to making sense of the surrounding world, because with the impairment of one sense (e.g., vision), the auditory information can compensate for the negative effects of the degraded visual one. Providing conditions that not only "permit," but rather "promote" supportive sonic environments could be beneficial for the well-being and quality of life of persons with dementia in care facilities. For this to happen, it is also necessary to raise awareness on this matter among the staff members working in the care sector [10,11]. Because of their "implicit knowledge about the role of the auditory environment into the daily practice of working with persons with an intellectual disability" [9], they may play a crucial role in improving this environment through changes in modus operandi, a knowledge gained in the group of people with intellectual disability and also applicable to people with dementia.

In this paper, a framework for improving the auditory environment by adding acoustic stimuli to an existing acoustic environment in order to obtain supportive effects for persons with dementia, is proposed. The paper starts with a narrative review of elements contributing in the interplay between perception, cognition and behavior. This leads to the main result, the definition of targeted effects which can be understood as contributing to behavior influencers and its presentation in a framework for soundscape design in nursing homes. This framework is then discussed in view of general aspects and in view of related studies where soundscape deployment in nursing homes has been experimented.

2. State of the Art

The design of a sonic environment in the context of a nursing home hosting persons with dementia requires taking into account the existing evidence in the field of auditory perception and related behavior with respect to ageing and cognition deficits, the state of the art of which is narratively reviewed here.

2.1. Perception: From Sonic Environment (Acoustic Scene) to Soundscape

Having defined the difference between a sonic environment and a soundscape, it is important to understand what makes the construction of the latter possible, descending from the former. Identifying how the mechanisms involved might be different for people with cognitive impairments will allow us to derive the design methodology. Due to the ubiquitous nature of sound, the scanning of all sounds present in a sonic environment demands a very high cognitive load, making a saliency mechanism in sound perception beneficial [12]. Auditory attention plays a key role in this process [13]. The ability of a sound to attract attention is in turn affected by a number of factors related to both the characteristics of the sound itself, as well as by personal traits of the listener, reflecting a bottom-up and top-down modulation of the attention mechanism. Attention can be modulated by 'bottom-up' stimulus-driven factors (e.g., a loud explosion sound), 'top-down' task-specific goals (e.g., in case of an announcement in a busy train station), expectations and learned schemas [14]. Although general attention is a multi domain modality making it necessary to account for multi sensory (visual) integration [15], the auditory attention mechanism remains in case of visual impairment. Sounds that are foregrounded by the attention and gating mechanisms will trigger associations. These are often related to sound sources or activities [16]. In a more general sense, these sounds have meaning. A simple interpretation of "meaning" could indeed be the collection of associations triggered by noticing a sound. Meaning is personal, but also has a cultural component. It can change over time through new experiences resulting in novel neural associations provided the plasticity of the brain is intact. The sonic environment, as a whole, also has the potential of creating meaning, changing mood, affect and emotion, irrespectively of whether it is split in separate auditory objects that receive attention. Music is by far the best-known example [17] but also natural and environmental sound environments may have music-like characteristics [18]. But even simple sounds can trigger an emotional response depending on their loudness and sharpness [19]. Appraisal of the soundscape involves the cognitive and emotional response described above related to personal expectations and frame of reference. Expectations in a shorter time frame influence the appraisal of the sonic environment [20], with moderate expectation violation creating the most pleasing environments. Liking and pleasure follow an inverse U curve with the degree of complexity or predictability of the environment (the Wundt curve). Very simple sonic environments, or cognitive and emotional journeys, are easily predicted and do not open up the possibility for learning. Very high complexity causes unpredictability and constant expectation violation, which also results in lower appraisal of the environment—the middle is just right. As experience grows, the inverse U curve shifts to higher complexities. A qualitative model relating sonic environment to soundscape is sketched in Figure 1 from Reference [21].

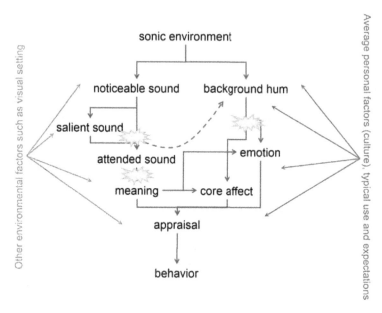

Figure 1. Human perception model: from sonic environment to soundscape appraisal (adapted from [21]). The surprise text balloons indicate some possible deficits resulting in e.g., deviant appraisal (upper left): impaired perception of sound features; (lower left): impaired recognition of sounds; (right): impaired perception of auditory scenes and objects.

2.2. Perceived Safety Theory

Following Maslow's hierarchy of needs, aside from essential physiological needs, safety is a basic need a person should fulfill [22]. Modern theories of perceived safety, such as the Generalized Unsafety Theory of Stress (GUTS), explain observations by assuming that the stress response is the default state that constantly needs to be inhibited [23,24]. Common situations where this is affecting behavior includes loneliness, low social status, adult life after prenatal or early life adversity, lack of a natural environment and less fit bodily states such as obesity or fatigue. Reflected to the context of nursing home residents with dementia, one could consider loneliness and lack of a natural environment as important situations. The absence of (environmental) signals that confirm safety may lead to chronic stress responses rather than the presence of instantaneous stressors. In this way, understanding where one is and understanding what time it is, will result in a behavior adapted to place and time. Since audition is the primary sense for detecting danger, it can be expected that the sonic environment has the power to influence perceived safety. Shäfer et al. [25] have shown the importance of stress and danger as perceived from music, silence and natural sounds (chirping crickets) in order to obtain indications of the environment, indicating that suitable music could be beneficial for this purpose.

2.3. Effects of Subliminal and Attended Sound on Behavior

The polarity of a sound with regard to its attended versus subliminal nature is giving two distinct ways to influence the behavior of a person. In a care setting where the use of sounds is considered, music therapy is an example of the behavior influencing potential of attended sounds. Music has been shown to give a manifold of positive effects, ranging from more physiological effects (arouse body temperature, reduce muscle tension, lower blood pressure, enhance depth breathing, elevate brain waves) to emotional or functional effects (influence emotion, decrease depression/improve mood, increase endurance and productivity, decrease anger, improve memory and learning, enhance sleep quality) [26,27]. Considering the emotional response, music is able to influence the mood and the emotions of a person and the 'Musical Mood Induction Procedure' (MMIP) [17] has gained a lot of attention and has shown that combined specific characteristics of the different musical elements (mode, tempo, pitch, rhythm, harmony and loudness) give rise to a range of emotional expressions (serious, sad, fear, serene, humorous, happy, exciting and majestic). In general, a slow tempo, low pitch and minor mode are associated with negative arousal and fast tempo, high pitch and major mode are associated with positive arousal. While music has a direct effect on mood its cognitive processing can also remind people of valued past events [28]. The initial mood is of importance in obtaining a high level of desired mood. Personal factors need to be taken into account, since individual differences occur from musical experience, preferences and traits. Indeed, it is important to state that music has a potential twofold outcome, as it can result in a positive or negative impact [26]. Apart from music, many different sounds can be present and take part in an acoustic scene. In general they can be classified following a detailed taxonomy of possible sound sources in a specific context (e.g., References [29,30]). A primary classification lies in the distinction between biophonic, geophonic and anthropogenic sounds. Nature and an associated natural sound environment have been shown to increase mental restoration after stressful periods [31] and the facilitation of mood recovery [32]. As components of nature, in a restorative environment one can consider 'being away' (giving rest in directed attention), fascination (freedom of thinking), extent (freedom) and compatibility (resulting in facilitating efforts) [33]. Bird sounds and birdsong in particular may contribute to a positive feeling, perceived restoration of attention and stress recovery [34–37]. For most people, natural sounds and birdsong in particular create a positive valence and are perceived as calm or vibrant [38].

2.4. Changing Auditory Processing and Cognition with Age

Age-related hearing loss (Presbycusis) is characterized by reduced hearing sensitivity (higher frequencies) and speech understanding in noisy environments, slowed central processing of acoustic information, and impaired localization of sound sources [39]. This disorder affects hearing in more than half of the elderly population and is known to influence the peripheral and cortical auditory processing. In older adults, the interplay between these processing centers leads to a more dominant distractability due to decreased afferent information regulation [40]. The resulting deficits are mainly in sound localization and temporal processing, which lead to poor speech perception. It has been shown that age-related deficits in the interhemispheric information processing may be at the origin of different hearing problems among the older people [41]. As for temporal origin, older people have a degraded hearing gap detection, which leads to missing elements in the segmental information of speech and results in degraded speech perception in noise [42]. Apart from the degeneration of the auditory system due to the ageing process itself, noise damage also takes part as a dominant factor. In addition, genetic susceptibility, otological disorders and the use of ototoxic drugs (like aminoglycosides, quinine, bèta blockers, non-steroidal anti-inflammatory agents and tricyclic antidepressants) can contribute to the decline in hearing [39,43]. Accumulated drug intake is the case in a significant group of older people [43]. As part of the binaural localization, the source position estimation results from processing inter-aural intensity differences and inter-aural time differences, which are affected by hearing loss [44]. In addition, the auditory distance perception in humans is based on sound level, degree of reverberation and frequency as primary cues and on non perceptual factors, including the importance of the auditory event to the listener [45,46]. The degree of reverberation (direct-to-reverberant energy ratio) is of obvious importance in an indoor context. In case of hearing loss, the use of sound level as a distance cue remains effective, the use of the degree of reverberation as distance cue becomes less effective [46]. It was evidenced that brain regions for sound localization and for sound identification processing are distinct [47], as many of these auditory deficits reflect the deteriorated activity of specific cortex regions. Hearing impairment has negative impacts on quality of life and daily functioning for older persons, as they affect conversation, music appreciation, orientation to alarms and participation in social activities [39,48] as was shown in an longitudinal study of more than 2500 subjects [49].

Although hearing aids and assistive devices can have a positive impact, hearing aid uptake in older adults remains low despite the significant technological progress in hearing aid technology over the last decade [50].

2.5. Deviant Auditory Processing and Resulting Behavior in Dementia

Symptoms of altered auditory cognition due to dementia induced brain changes were studied in a clinically oriented symptom-based approach by Hardy et al. [51], showing that these symptoms range from impaired perception of sound features to impaired higher cognitive tasks as the recognition of sounds, auditory scenes and objects:

- Impaired perception of sound features: this may manifest as cortical deafness or relatively selective 'word deafness' or auditory agnosia, more commonly described with progressive non fluent aphasia.
- Impaired recognition of sounds: due to erosion of semantic memory deficits of nonverbal sound recognition (auditory associative agnosia) like the recognition of environmental sounds are present in patients with semantic dementia, while for some individuals recognition of melodies preserves.
- Impaired perception of auditory scenes and objects: in this case difficulty following conversations and other sounds against background noise are reported, this may result in avoiding social interactions and a general dislike of complex auditory environments.
- Auditory hallucinations: Tinnitus as an elementary auditory hallucination is commonly reported by patients with semantic dementia. Muffled sounds or voices as hallucinations are often reported by patients with Lewy body dementia, as well as other musical hallucinations (comprising persistent familiar, basal tunes).
- Abnormal auditory behaviors: In this case, deviant emotional or hedonic behavioral responses to sound are observed in patients with dementia (due to impaired recognition of musical and nonverbal vocal emotions). Sound aversion is present in many patients of fronto-temporal dementia. On the other hand, abnormal craving for music (musicophilia) is associated with semantic dementia, these patients may show increased sensitivity to sound (hyperacusis).

Where speech and music are main sources when considering sound, several studies provide information and results related to the cognition of nonverbal sounds in dementia [52–54]. As reported, the findings provide evidence that separable stages of auditory object analysis and separable profiles of impaired auditory object cognition can be considered as they are encountered in different dementia syndromes. From these studies, it is clear that the wide spectrum of dementia results in a wide scale and levels of deviation in the "sound-cognition-behavior" interplay (as illustrated in Figure 1), and that from the underlying disease, the typical characteristics of the interplay can be considered, resulting in more or less distinct groups among the persons with dementia.

3. Soundscape Design Framework

In view of the above mentioned successes of music therapy and in view of the stated effects that the sonic environment may have on people, the suggestion is to carefully design the sonic environment in the place of residence of persons with dementia. In contrast to their peers in the same age category, these persons no longer have the ability to participate in events nor to create their own comfortable and/or stimulating environment. The main difference between soundscape design and music therapy lies in the continuous character of the sonic environment. To this end, a framework for designing a soundscape for persons with dementia is proposed that is based on the above narrative review and that is intended to be used in a soundscape intervention as is indicated in Figure 2.

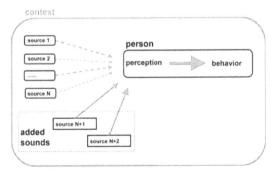

Figure 2. Schematic representation of the soundscape intervention introducing the added composed soundscape targeted to the desired behavioral response.

As previously described, it is clear that, due to dementia, different cognitive deficits can occur and can result in a perturbed sound perception, interpretation, appraisal and resulting behavior. While dementia is a syndrome of a wide window of cognitive deficits, it is a practical and attractive methodology to work with a limited number of distinguishable personas, which can identify the different over-all capabilities of the persons. In a first approach, a bi-level classification in interpreting and reacting capabilities of a person leads to an approach based on four personas [55,56]. Persons with a light form of dementia that has acceptable interpreting and reacting capabilities may benefit from making a wide variety of acoustic stimuli available to improve the stimuli-poor nursing home environment. For persons with reduced interpreting capabilities the sonic environment should be easy to disentangle. Explicit and clear meaning that may or may not relate to the past of the person should be beneficial. Not understanding the environment may lead to anxiety. These people may also lack the interpretation of time and space so sonic elements that help with understanding the day or the place may help. Persons with limited reacting capabilities may suffer from poor sonic environments while not being able to react appropriately. This may lead to behavior that is disturbing for other residents as well as for staff. Soundscapes may be more complex, diverse and challenging when interpretation capabilities are intact. The use of persona is motivated to account for a basic personalization of the resulting soundscape composition.

3.1. Designing for Effects

The evidence shows that an appropriate soundscape design could result in the following desired effects:

3.1.1. Mood Changers

The potential of using sound for changing mood will be discussed within the framework of the circumplex model of mood [57,58]. As a depressed mood is common for residents with dementia, supporting them to increase valence and/or arousal using specific sounds is attractive. Based on the evidence for music therapy, the mood changers in soundscape design can be understood as a time-elongated session of music therapy, where the sounds are played in the sleeping room or the living room of the residents. As an additional benefit a resulting positive mood has been shown to broaden the scope of auditory attention [59], giving desired outcomes in improved social interaction. With respect to arousal, mood changers may support the diurnal pattern of activities in the nursing home and help to synchronize inhabitants with this pattern. At specific times of the day, engaging and activating sounds may be beneficial while during other periods calming sounds may be beneficial. Sounds with a low level of meaning that may not even attract attention but that show fast fluctuations especially in the higher frequency range (e.g., a morning bird chorus) typically increase arousal and could be used for example, in the morning. Lower frequencies and slow variations, on the other hand, tend to reduce arousal and have a calming effect. In addition, the meaning associated with foregrounded sounds and music can indirectly influence mood, yet mainly along the valence dimension. When used for persons with dementia, special care is needed. When using music, the effect of rhythm seems to remain longer than lyrics during progression of dementia. Yet melody recognition may still be useful. In view of reduced capabilities to disentangle sounds and predicting what comes, lower complexity sonic environments are beneficial. Pleasure and thus the increase of valence are more likely to be related to these easy-to-predict-sonic environments than in healthy persons. Using the meaning associated with sounds or music for people with dementia remains challenging. Although using sounds from their past seem attractive for creating arousal, care should be taken not to reduce valence through associations that may not be known by the soundscape designer (e.g., music heard frequently during war times). Yet, in any case, meaning should be clear. Sounds that can not easily be interpreted without an explicit context (e.g., waves breaking on the shore) should be avoided. As a good rule-of-thumb, any sound that is expected to trigger associations should have an obvious and immediate meaning to the designer even if reproduced in poor conditions (as a proxy for reduced hearing capabilities). Considering the expected outcome of these mood changers, one can think of reduced medication intake through engaging, calming or activating residents.

3.1.2. Safety Enhancers

In order to enhance a safety feeling, basic stressors (like not knowing where one is and not knowing what time it is) need to be avoided while in line with the GUTS signals confirming safety should be provided continuously. Information about the current time and place is crucial with this respect. Auditory sources can give this information and can enhance the safety feeling in this way. As an example one can think of the church bells giving a specific sound each hour. Such a sound is easily recognized and incorporates the time information. The characteristics of the bell sound itself can even work as a spatial orientation sound, making it function as a soundmark in place and time orientation. Also in the framework of the GUTS sounds heard in the distance with a repeating character can confirm the presence of other people and the usual surrounding activity. Both biophonic and anthropogenic sounds could be used. This could be particularly important at the moment that the person with dementia is alone. Safety enhancers for people with dementia should be particularly clear and high fidelity sounds that can easily be recognized. Too much novelty should be avoided. Considering the expected outcome of these safety enhancers, one can think of more tranquil nights and better sleep quality (through relaxing and stabilizing a resident).

3.1.3. Response Triggers

A sound can be used to evoke a (Pavlovian) reaction in a way that specific behavior is initiated. For this reactive purpose, clear and unique sounds are required, which in general generate low level associations in the brain and trigger an autonomous like response. They can also take part in the nomic or symbolic mapping as a level of understanding the environment. Following the daytime activity patterns and personal habits, such sound elements are in general present in a person's nomic or symbolic map, as one can often relate specific sounds to the predicted and desired activity. In this way they arise from the life-long learning and experiencing of the temporal binding of daily sounds. In a home context, one can think of the typical sounds of cutlery or kitchen sounds as an indication that a meal is expected to follow. In the context of a nursing home, starting from the existing environment as experienced by a resident with dementia, amplification of nomic sounds and additional explicit symbols in the soundscape may be required. Considering the expected outcome of these these response triggers, one can think of enhanced efficiency through triggering, announcing and avoiding startle of a resident.

3.2. Soundscape Composition

With the objective to obtain an appropriate soundscape, a daylong pattern of added sounds needs to be composed. These sounds consist of elementary acoustic stimuli and are intended to improve behavior to be in correspondence with the diurnal activities. As added sounds are used in the continuous (24 h a day, 7 days a week) soundscape intervention, the desired outcome will benefit from a high-quality acoustic comfort and from the maximal avoidance of disturbing sounds. As designed sound environment will continue in perpetuity, residents will become habituated to these sonic environments and this new norm will become the confirmation of safety. As learning is very limited in persons with dementia, habituation could be less than for healthy persons. Still, switching off any added sound should be done carefully and only if unavoidable as this change may trigger unwanted behavior. The healthy brain may contain multiple representations of the world around it and use parallel predictive models, yet it is unsure how strongly this ability is preserved in all forms of dementia. In the daylong sound pattern, as depicted in Figure 3, the different elementary acoustic stimuli (including silent periods), the levels of which are between the typical background and foreground levels, are scheduled appropriate to the diurnal pattern and the personal aspects (persona). The sounds that are foreseen should be dominant and attract attention only if they are intended to trigger certain behavior. Mood changers and safety enhancers should be easy to suppress or background. Furthermore, the design of the sonic environment is intended to amend or replace the sounds that are typical for the institutionalized environment with sounds that are typical for an everyday living environment, the selection of which is supposed not to give person specific adverse reactions as can be assured from prior personal information or from staff observation and monitoring. The added sounds will be designed to mask undesired unit sounds if these are likely to trigger an unwanted response and are not enhancing perceived safety. In other situations, the added sound will create additional context for the sounds that are already present, modifying their meaning. In the context of a nursing home the resulting sound pattern can be delivered to the sleeping room of a resident or to a living room common for all residents. Where the soundscape composition for a common living room needs to take into account the presence of multiple residents, the composition in case of an individual sleeping room can be targeted towards the specific resident. Preferred sounds may change over time, for example because of the progression of the disease. As persons with dementia are generally not able to express their like or dislike nor to modify the playback system, a suitable playback system will need to rely on an evaluation of the state of the resident by a care giver. In view of efficiency, the soundscape intervention technology may benefit from an easily accessible feedback system and from staff participation in the operational aspects of the deployment. The determination of the diurnal pattern and the selection of the specific acoustic stimuli can result from participation of staff and residents as can be obtained during co-creation sessions. Designing an improved sonic environment for persons with dementia requires not only sufficient knowledge of the everyday context and the state of the residents, but also thorough insight into acoustics and psychoacoustics. This publication could only provide some suggestions, yet involving an acoustical expert in training the staff responsible for tuning and maintaining the sound playback is crucial.

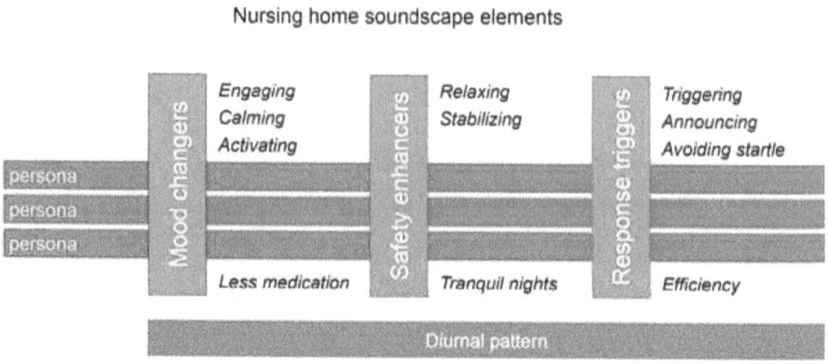

Nursing home soundscape elements

Figure 3. Representation of the nursing home soundscape design model, illustrating the 3 main behavior influencers with their expected outcomes, as scheduled over a diurnal pattern following the needs of a specific persona.

4. Discussion

In order to implement soundscapes for people with dementia, special requirements are needed to be fulfilled, in addition to basic standard guidelines.

As the intervention is intended to add acoustic stimuli to the existing soundscape, care should be taken that the resulting soundscape does not become chaotic. Sound levels of the added components need to be chosen in correspondence of the typical sound levels at the targeted places and with respect to the hearing capacity of a resident. The intention is to add sounds that mix in the level range between foreground and background levels. Indoor sound levels in nursing homes are reported for the different type of rooms present [10,60–62]. The existing soundscape in a nursing home (on the level of the living rooms) could often be described as giving an annoying, monotonous and uneventful perception [11]. This indicates that added acoustic stimuli could be deployed in these settings without obtaining a chaotic perception of the overall sonic environment.

In order to be effective, the deployment of the soundscape needs to take into account the foreground versus background characteristics and the timing aspects arising from diurnal temporal patterns. As a nursing home is an institution where staff is interacting with residents following their care needs, the anthropogenic soundscape component will follow the diurnal patterns arising from the organization of the care. In general, this follows a fixed daily pattern reflecting the different care and support activities (basic assistance such as helping patients bath, dress themselves, get up and down, walk, use of wheelchairs or walkers, food delivery, intake and administration of medication, support during social game sessions, …). Apart from the caregiver-resident interactions, the working schedule of the care givers with fixed moments of team shifts will also give rise to specific activity patterns. The diurnal composition of the delivered soundscape is beneficial through the support in the awareness of rhythms and routines of the residents, which is known to improve the care outcome [63].

In previous work [64], a pilot soundscape intervention study was conducted to experiment with composed soundscapes (Figure 4). In order to obtain maximal desired outcome, a study of the level of acoustic comfort present in the different nursing homes was performed, consisting of reverberation time measurements and sound insulation measurements between rooms, initiating interventions that have been realized to improve the acoustic comfort level in specific rooms [65,66]. During these experiments, different acoustic stimuli were selected to be part of a soundscape composition that was played continuously in individual rooms of residents. The selection and timing of these stimuli resulted from co-creation sessions with staff and family members. Staff need to be included in design changes and environmental interventions because this will stimulate staff cooperation and improve resident care. The resulting selected acoustic stimuli consisted of Birdsong (bird signing in natural context, light natural sounds as background) and Wind (light breeze in natural context and sounds of leaves rustling in the trees) during the morning, Bell (bell of a church marking the hour), Cafeteria (sounds of people chatting and cutlery) around noon, Typewriter (sound of a person writing, using a typing machine and little bell) in the afternoon, Music ("Claire de lune"—Debussy) towards the evening and a Heartbeat (sound of heartbeat with a rate of approximately 60–80 bpm) in the evening. A first evaluation of the experiments (living labs) was based on a qualitative interview on the impression of experiences of the health care professionals who worked with the soundscapes. Globally, the soundscapes were experienced as positive; the impact on the 'atmosphere' was obvious and consequently also on the behavior of the persons with dementia, mainly due to the 'orientating' function of the soundscape and under the condition that the soundscape is tailored made. A certain degree of 'habituation' was observed but this was not necessarily considered negative.

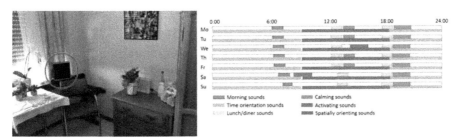

Figure 4. Illustration of a soundscape intervention: (**left**) photograph of a sleeping room setting with a soundscape player indicated with a red circle, (**right**) diurnal pattern of a composed soundscape with a weekly structure.

Where these sound tracks were selected during the co-creation sessions considering their appropriateness seen the timing characteristics and the specific nursing home context, they can also be considered in view of their supportive potential. Following the derived soundscape design framework a sound can contribute to the different desired effects in variable ways. This potential is illustrated in Figure 5 where the relative importance of the different desired effects (changing mood, stimulating the feeling of safety and triggering a response) is shown in a ternary plot, as resulted from a (subjective) single person assessment. The plot can be interpreted as a sound behavior influencing plot giving a visual interpretation of the behavior influencing effects of a sound in a specific context (specific place and time during the day) as is reflected in the ternary position and the influencing strength as is reflected in the saturation level of the color of the sound. A position more central in the triangle reflects a non-specific influencing sound, while a sound represented more to the corners indicates a sound with a specific influencing sound.

Taking into account the different possible deficits in the behavior pathway of a person with dementia, sounds should be intended to provide basic information in a redundant manner, as can be provided from both the foreground (meaning) pathway and the background (core affect) pathway. Considering that the different non musical sounds have a universal character and can be considered to have been present spread over a past lifetime, it can be expected that reminiscence [67], as originating from remaining long-term memory, can contribute in this way. The effect of ambient sound on the perceived safety was studied by Sayin et al. [68] and showed that when perceived social presence is higher and positive, the feeling-of-safety is also higher. In this view a typical bell sound of a church could act in this manner as it is intended to give an indication of an (active) community in the (perceived) neighborhood.

In understanding the role of sound on behavior, as is necessary in the design of a soundscape, one can also consider what is called a mind-state. Andringa et al. [69] described this approach as a model for describing the interaction between the core cognition and the peripheral sensing of a person. The interaction is described in a way that different arousal levels allow for different levels of mind-states. These levels range from a maximally restoring mind-state (sleep), over a restoring mind-state (characterized by fascination, automated tasks and automatic perception-action), an effortful mind-state (with novel tasks, directed attention and partial perception disengagement) to the highest arousal mind-state which is even effortful and even inefficient (from multitasking, directed attention switching and distractor claimed attention). Due to the cognitive deficits of persons with dementia, it can be expected from their activity levels that they mainly reside in a restoring mind-state. The use of an additional composed soundscape could help in stimulating and activating the residents towards a higher effortful mind-state.

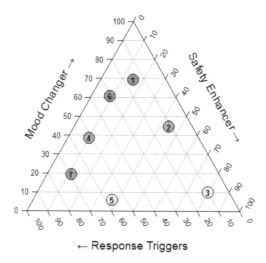

Figure 5. Ternary plot illustrating the mixing (relative importance indicated in percentages) of the mood, safety and response triggering aspects of the different acoustic stimuli: (1) Birdsong, (2) Wind, (3) Bell, (4) Cafetaria, (5) Typewriter, (6) Music, (7) Heartbeat as considered in a specific context. The saturation level of the color indicates the strength of the effects.

Due to the burden of dementia, a detailed diagnosis is often not available, which hinders the detailed personalization of the approach. In order to overcome this problem, a practical methodology combining bedside information with specific investigations was introduced which can lead to a clinical outcome which offers a ground for an added level of personalization [51]. Based on the knowledge of cognitive relations, such outcomes could indicate desired sound management characteristics resulting in personalized sound stimuli to be included in the composition.

5. Conclusions

Based on a narrative review of existing knowledge on the influence of the sonic environment on well-being and behavior and on the deviant processing of acoustic stimuli by people with dementia, this publication proposes designing supportive soundscapes for nursing home residents with dementia and forwards an appropriate design methodology. In addition to a classical acoustic design-for-comfort that includes appropriate sound insulation of the facade and between rooms, adequate absorption for reducing unwanted sound as well as improving speech intelligibility and reducing installation and operational noise, soundscape design also includes the permanent playback (24 h/7 days) of a sound composition in different rooms of the nursing home. One of the main reasons for adding these sounds is to influence the behavior of residents, to result in a decreased BPSD. The permanent character of the optimized sonic environment and the ubiquitous presence of such an intervention can make it an attractive mode of therapy as compared to the more common music therapy. It could enlighten the existing nursing home soundscape which is often perceived as annoying, monotonous and uneventful. The suggested design methodology proposes reflecting on three types of influences that the sonic environment could have—changing mood, increasing perceived safety and triggering responses. Both clearly noticeable sounds (triggering responses, perceived safety) and subliminal backgrounds (mood changers, perceived safety) could be used for these purposes. In view of the burden of different cognitive deficits, which take a specific role in the interplay between perception, cognition and behavior of persons with dementia and which come on top of the changing auditory processing and cognition with age, a few guidelines are proposed to the soundscape designer concerning the choice of sounds in his or her composition for this specific target group. Reduced capability of auditory scene analysis, gating and object formation should be considered and therefore complex sound environments should be avoided. Associative memory deficits may result in unexpected behavioral responses and, hence, care should be taken when meaningful sounds are used as mood changers or safety enhancers. With reduced plasticity, new response triggers may take longer than expected to be learned and hence the designer may attempt to rely on common historical symbolic or nomic mapping of sounds. As illustrated in the narrative review, dementia may take several forms some of which result in hefty and very different responses to sound ranging from sound aversion to musicophilia. Together, with the different meaning that could be given to sounds within the context of life long experience, this calls for a personalized approach to soundscape design. Co-creation involving care givers and persons from the direct surrounding (e.g., family) of the patient could be a beneficial in this respect. Technology could help by providing suitable interfaces to sound databases as well as opportunities for feedback. It is expected that an appropriate application of these ideas to the design of the living environment of nursing homes for people with dementia could reduce the use of pharmaceuticals and improve the working conditions for the staff in addition to improving the well-being of the residents.

Author Contributions: Conceptualization, all authors; methodology, all authors; investigation, all authors; writing–original draft preparation, P.D.; writing—review and editing, all authors; project administration, P.D., P.D.V., D.V.d.V., D.B.; funding acquisition, P.D., P.D.V., D.V.d.V., D.B. The contribution of one of the authors, F.A., took place during the AcustiCare project, while staying at Ghent University.

Funding: This paper is an outcome of the AcustiCare project, supported by the Flemish Agency for Innovation and Entrepreneurship (VLAIO) under the TETRA program for applied research (grant no. HBC.2016.0089), which was conducted from 1/10/2016 until 30/9/2018.

Acknowledgments: The authors are grateful to the staff members of the nursing homes for their support during the AcustiCare project, to the residents, and to their relatives.

Conflicts of Interest: The authors declare no conflict of interest.

References

1. World Health Organization. *Dementia: A Public Health Priority*; World Health Organization: Geneva, Switzerland, 2012.
2. Prince, M.; Bryce, R.; Albanese, E.; Wimo, A.; Ribeiro, W.; Ferri, C.P. The global prevalence of dementia: A systematic review and metaanalysis. *Alzheimer's Dement.* **2013**, *9*, 63–75. [CrossRef] [PubMed]
3. Ferri, C.P.; Prince, M.; Brayne, C.; Brodaty, H.; Fratiglioni, L.; Ganguli, M.; Hall, K.; Hasegawa, K.; Hendrie, H.; Huang, Y.; et al. Global prevalence of dementia: A Delphi consensus study. *Lancet* **2005**, *366*, 2112–2117. [CrossRef]
4. Livingston, G.; Sommerlad, A.; Orgeta, V.; Costafreda, S.G.; Huntley, J.; Ames, D.; Ballard, C.; Banerjee, S.; Burns, A.; Cohen-Mansfield, J.; et al. Dementia prevention, intervention, and care. *Lancet* **2017**, *390*, 2673–2734. [CrossRef]
5. Dijkstra, K.; Pieterse, M.; Pruyn, A. Physical environmental stimuli that turn healthcare facilities into healing environments through psychologically mediated effects: Systematic review. *J. Adv. Nurs.* **2006**, *56*, 166–181. [CrossRef]
6. ISO. *Acoustics—Soundscape—Part 1: Definition and Conceptual Framework*; Technical Report; ISO: Geneva, Switzerland, 2014.
7. Graham, M.E. Re-socialising sound: Investigating sound, selfhood and intersubjectivity among people living with dementia in long-term care. *Sound Stud.* **2018**, *5*, 175–190. [CrossRef]

8. Van den Bosch, K.A. Safe and Sound: Soundscape research in special needs care. *Gron. Univ. Gron.* **2015**, *13*, 61–68. [CrossRef]

9. Van den Bosch, K.A.; Andringa, T.C.; Başkent, D.; Vlaskamp, C. The Role of Sound in Residential Facilities for People With Profound Intellectual and Multiple Disabilities. *J. Policy Pract. Intellect. Disabil.* **2016**, *13*, 61–68. [CrossRef]

10. Aletta, F.; Botteldooren, D.; Thomas, P.; Vander Mynsbrugge, T.; De Vriendt, P.; Van de Velde, D.; Devos, P. Monitoring Sound Levels and Soundscape Quality in the Living Rooms of Nursing Homes: A Case Study in Flanders (Belgium). *Appl. Sci.* **2017**, *7*, 874. [CrossRef]

11. Aletta, F.; Vander Mynsbrugge, T.; Van de Velde, D.; De Vriendt, P.; Thomas, P.; Filipan, K.; Botteldooren, D.; Devos, P. Awareness of 'sound' in nursing homes: A large-scale soundscape survey in Flanders (Belgium). *Build. Acoust.* **2018**, *25*, 43–59. [CrossRef]

12. Kayser, C.; Petkov, C.I.; Lippert, M.; Logothetis, N.K. Mechanisms for Allocating Auditory Attention: An Auditory Saliency Map. *Curr. Biol.* **2005**, *15*, 1943–1947. [CrossRef]

13. Oldoni, D.; Coensel, B.D.; Boes, M.; Rademaker, M.; Baets, B.D.; Renterghem, T.V.; Botteldooren, D. A computational model of auditory attention for use in soundscape research. *J. Acoust. Soc. Am.* **2013**, *134*, 852–861. [CrossRef] [PubMed]

14. Kaya, E.M.; Elhilali, M. Modelling auditory attention. *Philos. Trans. R. Soc. B Biol. Sci.* **2017**, *372*, 20160101. [CrossRef] [PubMed]

15. Talsma, D.; Senkowski, D.; Soto-Faraco, S.; Woldorff, M.G. The multifaceted interplay between attention and multisensory integration. *Trends Cogn. Sci.* **2010**, *14*, 400–410. [CrossRef] [PubMed]

16. Raimbault, M.; Dubois, D. Urban soundscapes: Experiences and knowledge. *Cities* **2005**, *22*, 339–350. [CrossRef]

17. Västfjäll, D. Emotion induction through music: A review of the musical mood induction procedure. *Music. Sci.* **2001**, *5*, 173–211. [CrossRef]

18. Botteldooren, D.; Coensel, B.D.; Muer, T.D. The temporal structure of urban soundscapes. *J. Sound Vib.* **2006**, *292*, 105–123. [CrossRef]

19. Västfjäll, D. Emotional Reactions to Sounds without Meaning. *Psychology* **2012**, *3*, 606–609. [CrossRef]

20. Pearce, M.T.; Wiggins, G.A. Auditory Expectation: The Information Dynamics of Music Perception and Cognition. *Top. Cogn. Sci.* **2012**, *4*, 625–652. [CrossRef]

21. Filipan, K.; Boes, M.; Coensel, B.D.; Domitrovic, H.; Botteldooren, D. Identifying and recognizing noticeable sounds from physical measurements and their effect on soundscape. In Proceedings of the 10th European Congress and Exposition on Noise Control Engineering Euronoise 2015, Maastricht, The Netherlands, 31 May–3 June 2015.

22. Maslow, A.H. A theory of human motivation. *Psychol. Rev.* **1943**, *50*, 370–396. [CrossRef]

23. Brosschot, J.F.; Verkuil, B.; Thayer, J.F. Exposed to events that never happen: Generalized unsafety, the default stress response, and prolonged autonomic activity. *Neurosci. Biobehav. Rev.* **2017**, *74*, 287–296. [CrossRef]

24. Brosschot, J.; Verkuil, B.; Thayer, J. Generalized Unsafety Theory of Stress: Unsafe Environments and Conditions, and the Default Stress Response. *Int. J. Environ. Res. Public Health* **2018**, *15*, 464. [CrossRef] [PubMed]

25. Schäfer, T.; Huron, D.; Shanahan, D.; Sedlmeier, P. The sounds of safety: Stress and danger in music perception. *Front. Psychol.* **2015**, *6*. [CrossRef] [PubMed]

26. Iyendo, T.O. Exploring the effect of sound and music on health in hospital settings: A narrative review. *Int. J. Nurs. Stud.* **2016**, *63*, 82–100. [CrossRef] [PubMed]

27. Iyendo, T.O. Sound as a supportive design intervention for improving health care experience in the clinical ecosystem: A qualitative study. *Complement. Ther. Clin. Pract.* **2017**, *29*, 58–96. [CrossRef] [PubMed]

28. Sloboda, J.A.; ONeill, S.A.; Ivaldi, A. Functions of Music in Everyday Life: An Exploratory Study Using the Experience Sampling Method. *Music. Sci.* **2001**, *5*, 9–32. [CrossRef]

29. Salamon, J.; Jacoby, C.; Bello, J.P. A Dataset and Taxonomy for Urban Sound Research. In Proceedings of the ACM International Conference on Multimedia, MM 14, Orlando, FL, USA, 3–7 November 2014. [CrossRef]

30. Lindborg, P. A taxonomy of sound sources in restaurants. *Appl. Acoust.* **2016**, *110*, 297–310. [CrossRef]

31. Alvarsson, J.J.; Wiens, S.; Nilsson, M.E. Stress Recovery during Exposure to Nature Sound and Environmental Noise. *Int. J. Environ. Res. Public Health* **2010**, *7*, 1036. [CrossRef]

32. Benfield Jacob, A.; Derrick, T.B.; Peter, N.; Joshua, S. Natural Sound Facilitates Mood Recovery. *Ecopsychology* **2014**, *6*, 183–188. [CrossRef]
33. Kaplan, S. The restorative benefits of nature: Toward an integrative framework. *J. Environ. Psychol.* **1995**, *15*, 169–182. [CrossRef]
34. Mackrill, J.; Jennings, P.; Cain, R. Exploring positive hospital ward soundscape interventions. *Appl. Ergon.* **2014**, *45*, 1454–1460. [CrossRef]
35. Mackrill, J.; Cain, R.; Jennings, P. Experiencing the hospital ward soundscape: Towards a model. *J. Environ. Psychol.* **2013**, *36*, 1–8. [CrossRef]
36. Ratcliffe, E.; Gatersleben, B.; Sowden, P.T. Bird sounds and their contributions to perceived attention restoration and stress recovery. *J. Environ. Psychol.* **2013**, *36*, 221–228. [CrossRef]
37. Ratcliffe, E.; Gatersleben, B.; Sowden, P.T. Associations with bird sounds: How do they relate to perceived restorative potential? *J. Environ. Psychol.* **2016**, *47*, 136–144. [CrossRef]
38. Axelsson, Ö.; Nilsson, M.E.; Berglund, B. A principal components model of soundscape perception. *J. Acoust. Soc. Am.* **2010**, *128*, 2836–2846. [CrossRef] [PubMed]
39. Gates, G.A.; Mills, J.H. Presbycusis. *Lancet* **2005**, *366*, 1111–1120. [CrossRef]
40. Stothart, G.; Kazanina, N. Auditory perception in the aging brain: The role of inhibition and facilitation in early processing. *Neurobiol. Aging* **2016**, *47*, 23–34. [CrossRef] [PubMed]
41. Martin, J.S.; Jerger, J.F. Some effects of aging on central auditory processing. *J. Rehabil. Res. Dev.* **2005**, *42*, 25–44. [CrossRef]
42. Pichora-Fuller, M.K.; Singh, G. Effects of age on auditory and cognitive processing: Implications for hearing aid fitting and audiologic rehabilitation. *Trends Amplif.* **2006**, *10*, 29–59. [CrossRef]
43. Howarth, A.; Shone, G.R. Ageing and the auditory system. *Postgrad. Med. J.* **2006**, *82*, 166–171. [CrossRef]
44. Ross, B.; Fujioka, T.; Tremblay, K.L.; Picton, T.W. Aging in Binaural Hearing Begins in Mid-Life: Evidence from Cortical Auditory-Evoked Responses to Changes in Interaural Phase. *J. Neurosci.* **2007**, *27*, 11172–11178. [CrossRef]
45. Bronkhorst, A.W.; Houtgast, T. Auditory distance perception in rooms. *Nature* **1999**, *397*, 517–520. [CrossRef] [PubMed]
46. Kolarik, A.J.; Moore, B.C.J.; Zahorik, P.; Cirstea, S.; Pardhan, S. Auditory distance perception in humans: A review of cues, development, neuronal bases, and effects of sensory loss. *Atten. Percept. Psychophys.* **2016**, *78*, 373–395. [CrossRef]
47. Ahveninen, J.; Huang, S.; Nummenmaa, A.; Belliveau, J.W.; Hung, A.Y.; Jääskeläinen, I.P.; Rauschecker, J.P.; Rossi, S.; Tiitinen, H.; Raij, T. Evidence for distinct human auditory cortex regions for sound location versus identity processing. *Nat. Commun.* **2013**, *4*, 2585. [CrossRef] [PubMed]
48. Fortunato, S.; Forli, F.; Guglielmi, V.; De Corso, E.; Paludetti, G.; Berrettini, S.; Fetoni, A.R. A review of new insights on the association between hearing loss and cognitive decline in ageing. *Acta Otorhinolaryngol. Ital.* **2016**, *36*, 155–166. [PubMed]
49. Wallhagen, M.I.; Strawbridge, W.J.; Shema, S.J.; Kurata, J.; Kaplan, G.A. Comparative Impact of Hearing and Vision Impairment On Subsequent Functioning. *J. Am. Geriatr. Soc.* **2001**, *49*, 1086–1092. [CrossRef]
50. Meister, H.; Rählmann, S.; Walger, M.; Margolf-Hackl, S.; Kießling, J. Hearing aid fitting in older persons with hearing impairment: The influence of cognitive function, age, and hearing loss on hearing aid benefit. *Clin. Interv. Aging* **2015**, *10*, 435. [CrossRef]
51. Hardy, C.J.D.; Marshall, C.R.; Golden, H.L.; Clark, C.N.; Mummery, C.J.; Griffiths, T.D.; Bamiou, D.E.; Warren, J.D. Hearing and dementia. *J. Neurol.* **2016**, *263*, 2339–2354. [CrossRef]
52. Goll, J.C.; Kim, L.G.; Hailstone, J.C.; Lehmann, M.; Buckley, A.; Crutch, S.J.; Warren, J.D. Auditory object cognition in dementia. *Neuropsychologia* **2011**, *49*, 2755–2765. [CrossRef]
53. Goll, J.C.; Kim, L.G.; Ridgway, G.R.; Hailstone, J.C.; Lehmann, M.; Buckley, A.H.; Crutch, S.J.; Warren, J.D. Impairments of auditory scene analysis in Alzheimer's disease. *Brain J. Neurol.* **2012**, *135*, 190–200. [CrossRef]
54. Fletcher, P.D.; Nicholas, J.M.; Downey, L.E.; Golden, H.L.; Clark, C.N.; Pires, C.; Agustus, J.L.; Mummery, C.J.; Schott, J.M.; Rohrer, J.D.; et al. A physiological signature of sound meaning in dementia. *Cortex* **2016**, *77*, 13–23. [CrossRef]
55. Vander Mynsbrugge, T.; Van de Velde, D.; Aletta, F.; Botteldooren, D.; Devos, P.; De Vriendt, P. A model of soundscape for people with dementia living in nursing homes. In Proceedings of the WFOT Congress 2018, Cape Town, South Africa, 21–25 May 2018.

56. De Vriendt, P.; Vander Mynsbrugge, T.; Aletta, F.; Botteldooren, D.; Devos, P.; Van de Velde, D. Developing a method for soundscape design for people with dementia living in nursing homes: Validation of four persona. *Int. Psychogeriatr.* **2019**, *31*, 58.

57. Russell, J.A. A circumplex model of affect. *J. Personal. Soc. Psychol.* **1980**, *39*, 1161–1178. [CrossRef]

58. Posner, J.; Russell, J.A.; Peterson, B.S. The circumplex model of affect: An integrative approach to affective neuroscience, cognitive development, and psychopathology. *Dev. Psychopathol.* **2005**, *17*. [CrossRef] [PubMed]

59. Putkinen, V.; Makkonen, T.; Eerola, T. Music-induced positive mood broadens the scope of auditory attention. *Soc. Cogn. Affect. Neurosci.* **2017**, *12*, 1159–1168. [CrossRef]

60. Peng, J.; Zeng, Y.; Zhao, L.; Zeng, J. An investigation of acoustical environments in the elderly care facilities. *Appl. Acoust.* **2018**, *137*, 45–50. [CrossRef]

61. Brown, J.; Fawzi, W.; Shah, A.; Joyce, M.; Holt, G.; McCarthy, C.; Stevenson, C.; Marange, R.; Shakes, J.; Solomon-Ayeh, K. Low stimulus environments: Reducing noise levels in continuing care. *BMJ Qual. Improv. Rep.* **2016**, *5*, u207447-w4214. [CrossRef]

62. Jerlehag, C.; Lee, P.J.; Park, S.H.; Jones, T.; Carroll, N. Acoustic environments of patient room in a typical geriatric ward. *Appl. Acoust.* **2018**, *133*, 186–193. [CrossRef]

63. Riche, Y.; Mackay, W. PeerCare: Supporting Awareness of Rhythms and Routines for Better Aging in Place. *Comput. Supported Coop. Work* **2010**, *19*, 73–104. [CrossRef]

64. Devos, P.; Aletta, F.; Thomas, P.; Filipan, K.; Petrovic, M.; Botteldooren, D.; Vander Mynsbrugge, T.; Van de Velde, D.; De Vriendt, P. Soundscape Design for Management of Behavioral Disorders: A Pilot Study among Nursing Home Residents with Dementia. In Proceedings of the Internoise 2018 Conference, Chicago, IL, USA, 26–29 August 2018.

65. Thomas, P.; Aletta, F.; Vander Mynsbrugge, T.; Filipan, K.; Dijckmans, A.; De Geetere, L.; Botteldooren, D.; Petrovic, M.; De Vriendt, P.; Van de Velde, D.; et al. Evaluation and improvement of the acoustic comfort in nursing homes: A case study in Flanders, Belgium. In Proceedings of the 11th European Congress and Exposition on Noise Control Engineering (Euronoise 2018), Crete, Greece, 27–31 May 2018; pp. 405–412.

66. Thomas, P.; Aletta, F.; Filipan, K.; Mynsbrugge, T.V.; Geetere, L.D.; Dijckmans, A.; Botteldooren, D.; Petrovic, M.; de Velde, D.V.; Vriendt, P.D.; et al. Noise environments in nursing homes: An overview of the literature and a case study in Flanders with quantitative and qualitative methods. *Appl. Acoust.* **2020**, *159*, 107103. [CrossRef]

67. Dihkel, T.R. Rumination and reminiscence in older adults: Implications for clinical practice. *Eur. J. Ageing* **2013**, *10*, 223–227. [CrossRef]

68. Sayin, E.; Krishna, A.; Ardelet, C.; Briand Decré, G.; Goudey, A. "Sound and safe": The effect of ambient sound on the perceived safety of public spaces. *Int. J. Res. Mark.* **2015**, *32*, 343–353. [CrossRef]

69. Andringa, T.C.; Lanser, J.J.L. How pleasant sounds promote and annoying sounds impede health: A cognitive approach. *Int. J. Environ. Res. Public Health* **2013**, *10*, 1439–1461. [CrossRef] [PubMed]

International Journal of
*Environmental Research
and Public Health*

Review

The Impact of Green Space on Violent Crime in Urban Environments: An Evidence Synthesis

Mardelle Shepley [1,*], Naomi Sachs [1,2], Hessam Sadatsafavi [3], Christine Fournier [4] and Kati Peditto [1]

[1] Department of Design & Environmental Analysis, Cornell University, Ithaca, NY 14850, USA; nsachs@healinglandscapes.org (N.S.); ksp66@cornell.edu (K.P.)
[2] Department of Plant Science and Landscape Architecture, University of Maryland, College Park, MD 20742, USA
[3] Department of Emergency Medicine, University of Virginia School of Medicine, Charlottesville, VA 22908, USA; hs8pb@virginia.edu
[4] Mann Library, Cornell University, Ithaca, NY 14850, USA; ctf43@cornell.edu
* Correspondence: mshepley@cornell.edu

Received: 31 October 2019; Accepted: 12 December 2019; Published: 14 December 2019

Abstract: Can the presence of green space in urban environments reduce the frequency of violent crime? To ascertain the evidence on this topic, we conducted an in-depth literature review using the PRISMA checklist. The search parameters included US articles written in English and published since 2000. More than 30,000 potential paper titles were identified and ultimately, 45 papers were selected for inclusion. Green spaces typically comprised tree cover, parks and ground cover. Criminal behaviors typically included murder, assault, and theft. The majority of the research reviewed involved quantitative methods (e.g., comparison of green space area to crime data). We extracted multiple mechanisms from the literature that may account for the impact of green space on crime including social interaction and recreation, community perception, biophilic stress reduction, climate modulation, and spaces expressing territorial definition. Recommendations are made for future research, such as meta-analysis of existing data and the development of grounded theory through qualitative data-gathering methods. By providing evidence that access to nature has a mitigating impact on violence in urban settings, city governments and communities are empowered to support these interventions.

Keywords: violent crime; urban parks; greenspace; green space; scoping review; systematic review; literature review

---

1. Introduction

In this literature review, we investigate whether the presence of nature in urban environments reduce the frequency of violent crime. Research suggests that, in many circumstances, green space in the form of trees, parks, and other natural areas, may have a mitigating impact. By providing evidence that the presence of nature contributes to the reduction of violence in urban settings, city governments and communities will be empowered to support these interventions.

The positive impact of nature and green space on human health and well-being has been documented by over 100 studies [1–3], including several literature reviews and meta-analyses which have examined the benefits of the nature connection [2,4–10]. Several researchers have begun to explore the relationship between nature and urban crime, focusing on outcomes such as reduced aggression and improved community cohesion [11–14]. Multiple new papers and dissertations have been published in the last three years [15,16], and an expansive update is essential to setting future research agenda.

The following paper synthesizes the evidence of the impact of green space on violence by utilizing methods from systematic and scoping reviews. We are both addressing a specific question and describing the broader literature. A systematic review incorporates "appropriate" study designs that are pre-identified and include a paper quality assessment, which the research in this paper also undertakes [17]. A scoping review shares similar methods and aims, although the scoping review is concerned with presenting the characteristics of existing literature on a topic, whereas a systematic review aims to summarize the "best available research" on a topic [18].

Although violent crime in the United States has fallen since 1997 [19], Grinshteyn and Hemenway found that in 2010, the US gun homicide rate was 25 times higher than the rate in other high-income countries despite a similar rate of nonlethal crimes [20]. The study also reported that Americans are ten times more likely to die by firearms compared with residents of other countries. While many of these crimes are homicides, approximately 60% are suicides [21]. Additionally, there has been an increase in mass shootings. In 1994–2004, the average annual rate of mass shootings was 1.12 shooting per 100 million, while in 2005–2013, the average annual rate was 1.41 shooting per 100 million [22].

1.1. Definitions

According to Pati and Lorusso [23], one of the major challenges in conducting a systematic literature review is identifying the search terms. In this paper, the two primary categories were "green space" and "violent crime."

Greenspace. Green space is defined as "synonymous with nature" and "explicitly urban vegetation" [24]. In reviewing a range of journals, the authors identified many related terms including garden, ecological garden, urban forest, urban parks, urban habitat, greenery, greenbelt, green area, green environments, green network, green infrastructure, natural environment, parkland, walkable area, blue space, green patches, riparian greenspace, sky garden trees, urban farm, urban ecosystem, water bodies, woodland, and vegetated areas. This study uncovered six definitions of green space in the literature:

- Vegetation, ranging from sparsely landscaped streets to tree-lined walkways to playfields and forest parks [25].
- Combined areas of open land, cropland, urban open land, pasture, forest, and woody perennial [26].
- Land use that has notable contributions to urban environments in terms of ecology, aesthetics, or public health, but which basically serves human needs and uses [27].
- Areas with substantial green elements [28].
- Recreational or undeveloped land [29].
- Predominantly covered with vegetation [30].

Informed by this analysis, we defined green space using the broad description provided by the US Environmental Protection Agency (EPA). According to the EPA, green space is "land that is partly or completely covered with grass, trees, shrubs, or other vegetation ... Green space includes parks, community gardens, and cemeteries" [31].

Violent crime. The U.S. Department of Justice Federal Bureau of Investigation, in their Uniform Crime Reporting (UCR) program, defines violent crime as "composed of four offenses: murder and nonnegligent manslaughter, forcible rape, robbery, and aggravated assault. Violent crimes are defined in the UCR Program as "those offenses which involve force or threat of force" [32].

1.2. Goals

We have three goals associated with this research. First, to assess through a literature review where we stand with regard to studies that address the question: Can the presence of nature in urban environments reduce violent crime? Second, to generate an agenda for future research based on the gaps that are identified as part of this assessment. Lastly, to explore the mechanisms that might account for the interaction between urban nature and violent crime.

2. Materials and Methods

Using the PRISMA (Preferred Reporting Items for Systematic Reviews and Meta-Analyses) checklist [33], the authors drafted a plan for the literature review. Those articles written in English, published since 2000, and covering research in urban areas (not rural or suburban) within the United States were eligible for inclusion. The independent variable had to include at least one type of green space. At least one of the dependent variables had to be violent crime. No age, sex, socio-economic, health, or gender limitations were placed on study participants. The focus of the search was on original, primary peer-reviewed literature, although doctoral dissertations and master's theses, white papers, conference proceedings, and articles from organization websites were also eligible. Literature reviews were excluded because they were not primary research. No meta-analysis was undertaken because a range of research types (experimental, quasi-experimental, interventional, non-interventional, qualitative, quantitative, case study, cross-sectional, and longitudinal studies) was eligible for inclusion. Conflicting opinions about the relevance of a particular paper were resolved by a third, independent reviewer. The independent reviewer was blind to who had made the evaluation and the motivations for making the decisions, thus enhancing the validity of the evaluations.

2.1. Search Strategy and Database Selection

Databases were selected based on relevance and journal coverage. Subject area specific databases were identified, and a broad interdisciplinary database (Scopus) was also searched. Initial searches took place in December 2017 with updates to the searches run in July 2019. Using the EBSCOhost research platform, a joint search was performed on PsycINFO, Academic Search Premier, and Greenfile. Sociological Abstracts and ProQuest Dissertations and Theses–Global were searched jointly using ProQuest. The results of the searches were de-duplicated using Zotero reference software and then uploaded to Covidence (a systematic review platform), where another round of de-duplication took place. One deviation from the protocol was that title screening for inclusion or exclusion took place ahead of traditional abstract screening because of the large volume of results. Following initial blinded title screening in Covidence, the authors switched to Rayyan, another systematic review platform, for all subsequent screening. Full-text articles emerging from the screening process were evaluated by the authors and eliminated at that stage if they did not meet inclusion criteria.

Search terms were drafted using keywords and terms from papers known to be relevant to the review. Following testing in the chosen databases, the following terms were used in all searches, though the syntax of the search was adapted per database requirements as necessary:

(urban OR cities OR city OR neighborhood OR communit * OR "public housing *")

AND

("green space *" OR green * OR greenspace OR park * OR natur * OR "landscape architecture *" OR "city plan *" OR tree * OR "environment * design" OR ecosystem * OR environment * OR "urban design" OR horticulture OR playground OR garden OR trail OR "urban forestry")

AND

(crime * OR criminology OR violence OR rape * OR assault OR murder OR aggression OR firearm * OR gun * OR "public safe *")

2.2. Evaluation Process

Two researchers independently screened the titles and abstracts. A third researcher resolved conflicting decisions. Once the final list of papers was established, they were reviewed by the same two researchers to confirm that they were appropriate for inclusion. As previously, when the two paper reviewers disagreed on their evaluation, a third reviewer broke the tie. Once the final list of papers was determined, the three researchers entered summary information into a common spreadsheet, which was later distilled into a literature matrix (see Appendix A).

3. Results

3.1. PRISMA Summary

In January 2018 and July 2019, 31,414 records were identified via the database search ($n = 21{,}704$ in 2018 and $n = 9710$ in 2019). Excluding duplicates, 14,520 titles were ultimately screened. After the subsequent title screening, 3798 abstracts remained as potentially relevant publications. After the abstract review, 327 articles were selected for evaluation. Ultimately, 45 papers were selected for inclusion in this study, representing a little over 1% of the original abstracts (see Figure 1).

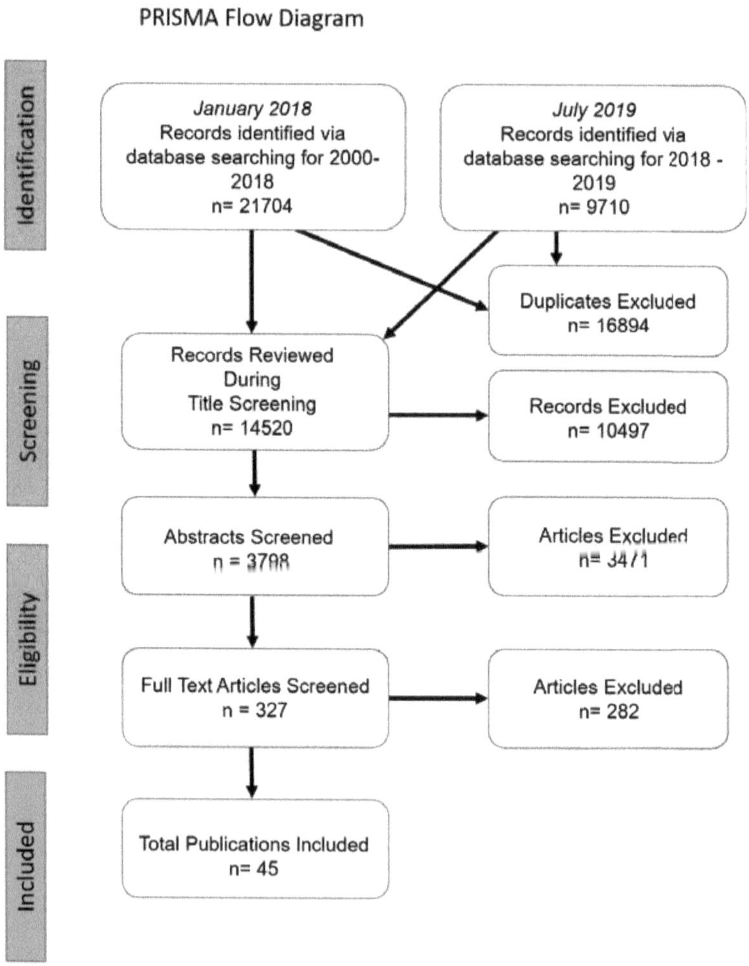

PRISMA Flow Diagram

Figure 1. Preferred Reporting Items for Systematic Reviews and Meta-Analyses (PRISMA) flow chart.

3.2. Patterns in Study Topics and Methods

Green space independent variables fell into five main categories: (1) parks, (2) community gardens and vacant lot remediation, (3) vegetated/tree-lined streets and walkways (including elevated trails), (4) tree canopies and groundcover, and (5) undeveloped or partially developed areas such as ground sewer enhancements, croplands, wetlands, undeveloped nature environments and landscape diversity endeavors (see Table 1).

Criminal behaviors typically addressed by researchers included homicide, assault (including rape), and theft (burglary). Most studies involved both violent personal crime and non-violent property crime (e.g., theft and vandalism). Several studies included disorderly crime, like narcotics use or distribution.

The majority of the 45 selected articles used quantitative methods. Quantitative studies tended to use ArcGIS or other spatial-image analysis tools to assess the presence of parks, vacant lots, or tree canopy. Most studies sought to correlate GIS/image data with jurisdictional crime data. Studies involving tree cover were correlational because almost all employed GIS or image-related data instead of interventions. A few studies predicted causality by employing before and after greening interventions (e.g., greening blighted lots, installing an elevated trail).

Much of the literature we reviewed and decided to omit was anecdotal, although we were interested in high-quality qualitative studies. Only a handful of studies used qualitative methods. Branas et al., Blair, and Garvin et al. employed a mixed-methods approach by combining quantitative crime analyses with interviews or surveys to assess perceptions of crime and neighborhood disorder [34–36]. While most studies included in the scope of this review used jurisdictional crime data, a few research teams used survey measures to assess the risk of aggressive behavior or perceptions of crime and safety.

When considering the methodological challenges shared between these studies, homicide and forcible rape were excluded from the analysis of violent crime in some studies (e.g., Wolfe and Mennis [37]), as these incidents are relatively few. In the case of rape, the data is questionable for other reasons; researchers noted that measuring the frequency of rape is misleading due to the low levels of formal reporting [38].

3.3. Study Findings

For studies involving a large range of violent crimes, the most consistent results aligning nature interventions and crime reduction were among studies involving vegetated streets and walkways. As might be expected, the majority of all studies were correlational, and the quasi-experimental studies involving greening interventions were typically limited to community gardens and site greening interventions, likely due to the scale of these projects. Several notable exceptions include the street/walkway improvements research described by Locke et al. [39] and the lot improvements performed by Branas et al. in Philadelphia [11,34,40].

As indicated in Table 1, of the 26 studies addressing all violent crimes, 12 identified a negative relationship between nature and crime (such that crime decreased as nature increased), while four ran contrary to our expectation. Ten studies were deemed inconclusive by their respective authors, as the results did not reach statistical significance or involved a number of confounds. With regard to violent crime (not involving homicide or rape), four of the six relevant studies demonstrated nature's contribution to crime reduction. The single study specifically focused on homicide [41] found reductions in homicide in parks, although the results regarding the impact of remediated sites were inconclusive.

Studies that focused specifically on gun violence support the hypothesis that green space reduces this violence [11,34,36,40,42–46]. Of the nine studies (two reported in a single publication by Branas et al. [11]), six had the expected outcomes. Three of the 45 studies were from the same team of researchers (Branas, Kondo, South) who investigated the potential link between green space and crime through the cleaning and greening of vacant lots, primarily in Philadelphia, PA.

3.3.1. Parks

Ten studies addressed the relationship between parks and crime, though all of these studies were correlational and did not study a specific intervention. Three studies found that the presence of parks was associated with reductions in crime, two were inconclusive, and three demonstrated trends in the opposite direction (Abu-Lughod [47], Kim and Hipp [48], and McCord and Houser [49]). Abu-Lughod found that violent crime increased as the number of city-owned parks increased while Kim and Hipp and McCord and Houser suggest that areas near parks experienced higher levels of crime and disorder. These findings may be explained by Jane Jacobs' "eyes on the street" theory [50] and C. Ray Jeffrey's Crime Prevention through Environmental Design (CPTED) principles [51], such that an open public place where strangers may be less easily identified by members of the community may create opportunities for crime. McCord and Houser support this explanation, specifically addressing the guardianship theory in their study.

Overall, regarding parks, there are insufficient studies to reflect on the impact on violent crime (not homicide or rape), homicide only, and gun violence. None of the studies in these categories involved interventions, possibly due to the construction cost of a large park intervention and the delays in the development of landscape growth once a park was in place.

3.3.2. Community Gardens/Greening

A larger number of studies (*n* = 12) addressed community gardens and greening of lots. All of these studies suggested that greening interventions or the presence of community gardens were related to a reduction in crime. Included in this group is a series of pre-post studies by Branas et al. in which researchers "cleaned and greened" a series of lots over several years in Philadelphia, PA, resulting in decreased incidence of gun violence [11,34,40]. Heinze et al. [52], Kondo et al. [53], and Sadler et al. [54] also reported similar results from vacant lot greening interventions. The overall positive effects of blighted lot remediation (compared to the mixed results from parks) may also be attributed to CPTED and defensible space theories, such that the removal of abandoned buildings and overgrown brush reduces the amount of shelter and improves visual guardianship of an area.

Interventions (*n* = 7) were most common in this category, likely due to the lower fiscal and physical challenges associated with creating community gardens and greening—they are easier to add to the urban fabric. Branas et al. suggest that their interventions in Philadelphia were inexpensive, scalable, and readily executed in low-income residential areas [11].

3.3.3. Vegetated Streets and Walkways

Although we found a limited number of studies on the impact of vegetated streets and walkways (*n* = 6), all of them support the hypothesis that this type of green space influences crime. Four of the six studies involving vegetated streets found decreases in crime, while crime remained unchanged in the Auchincloss [55] and Locke [39] et al. studies. Auchincloss et al. suggest greenways require associated comprehensive social interventions in order to be effective. Locke et al. raised concerns surrounding the spillover effects, such as a reduction in crime around greened streets may simply spread to perimeter areas. Indeed, Branas et al. echoed this concern in their blighted lot greening studies [11]. Null findings may also be the result of poor operationalization of green space or selection bias in the greening process such that community partners may have not been random in their choice of streets on which to plant trees [39].

Included in the group are four quasi-experimental studies (Auchincloss et al. [55], Harris et al. [56], Harris [57], and Crewe [58]). Quasi-experimental studies were particularly common in this category, as most were pre–post studies examining the influence of a newly established greenway on crime in surrounding areas, including Philadelphia's 58th St Greenway (Auchincloss et al.), Chicago's Bloomingdale Trail (Harris et al.), and Boston's Southwest Corridor (Crewe).

3.3.4. Trees and Ground Cover

The largest number of studies fell into the category of trees and ground cover (*n* = 14), perhaps due to ease of analysis from readily available GIS data. Aerial GIS information can provide detailed information on large-scale urban vegetation and may allow for examination over time due to the natural growth of vegetation. As such, most studies were correlational—none of the studies involved large-scale greening interventions, but they often involved substantially larger datasets than studies in the previous categories. Many papers reported results from geographic and crime data involving entire cities, including Austin, Baltimore, Chicago, Milwaukee, New Haven, Philadelphia, and Portland. Donahue used GIS tools to investigate tree cover in over 200 cities (and 59 individual communities within one city) [59].

The majority of the papers described in this category reflect decreases in crime ($n = 9$), with four others reporting inconclusive results. Of the inconclusive, two revealed nuances in the relationship between urban green space and crime. In their investigation of population density and crime, Lim found a significant moderating effect of vegetation on crime rates, such as high vegetation buffering the influence of high density on violent crime, providing support for cognitive restoration theories [60]. Li also observed a moderated relationship, such as view-blocking vegetation being associated with more violent crime but less property crime [61]. Just as Auchincloss et al. suggested, greenway interventions must be accompanied by appropriate policy changes [55]. Donahue also provides evidence for the importance of implementation plans accompanying urban tree cover interventions [59].

3.3.5. Undeveloped Green Areas (and Other)

Studies by Kondo et al. [45] and Sparks [62] did not demonstrate significant or conclusive relationships. They were placed under this heading due to the uniqueness of the independent variables that they measured. The Kondo study focused on green stormwater infrastructure and the Sparks study focused on land use diversity such as wetlands, forested land, agricultural land, and barren land. The inclusion of these studies highlight the methodological challenges and nuances associated with green space studies, as the operationalization of greenspace can take many different forms.

Table 1. Literature Review Matrix by Predictors and Outcomes.

	All Violent Crime	Violent Crime (Not Homicide or Rape)	Homicide Only	Gun Violence
Parks	Abu-Lughod ('06) ° ↑ Blair et al. ('17) ° ~ Brown ('18) ° ↓ Lee ('13) ° ~ M⎯ord et al. ('17) † ↑ ⎯tkowski ('17) ° ↓	Boessen et al. ('18) ° ~ Kim et al. ('18) ° ↑	Culyba et al. ('16) ° ↓	DeMotto et al. ('06) ° ~
Community gardens/greening	Blair ('14) † ♦ ~ Blair et al. ('17) ° ~ Gorham et al. ('09) ° ♦ ~ Heinze et al. ('18) Δ ↓ Kondo et al. ('16) Δ ↓ Sadler et al. ('17) Δ ↓ Wilcox et al. ('13)		Culyba et al. ('16) ° ~	Branas et al. ('11) Δ ↓ Branas et al. ('16) Δ ↓ Branas et al. ('18) Δ ♦ ↓ Garvin et al. ('13) Δ ♦ ~
Vegetated streets and walkways	Auchincloss ('19) † ~ Burley ('18) ° ↓ ~ Harris et al. ('18) † ↑ ⎯arris ('18) † ♦ ↓ L⎯e et al. ('17) Δ ~	Crewe ('01) † ♦		
Trees and ground cover	Donahue et al. ('11) ° ~ Gilstad-Hayden ('15) ° ↓ Kondo et al. ('17-A) † ↓ Kuo et al. ('01) † ↓ Li ('08) ° ~ ⎯im ('05) ~ Sch⎯ler et al. ('18) ° ~ Snel⎯ve et al. ('04) ° ↓	Deng ('15) ° ~ Donovan et al. ('12) ° ↓ Wolfe et al. ('12) ° ↓		Troy et al. ('12) ° ↓ Troy et al. ('16) ° ↓ Kondo et al. ('17-B) † ↑
Undeveloped green areas	Sparks ('11) ° ~			Kondo et al. ('15) Δ ~

Study Design: ° Correlational, † Quasi-experimental (pre-post or control group); Δ Greening intervention; ♦ Included a qualitative component; Findings: ↓ Negative relationship between green space and crime; ↑ Positive relationship between green space and crime; ~ Inconclusive or no significant relationship found; Strictly qualitative studies excluded from this matrix but included in Appendix A.

28

4. Discussion

4.1. State of the Research

Research on the impact of green space crime is limited. Among the prominent findings of this hybrid review was that potentially confounding variables are rarely addressed in detail. This challenge may be related to the lack of a mutually agreed upon grounded theory linking independent, covariate, and depending variables. Relatedly, a prominent conclusion when reviewing the study findings is that, with the exception of a few studies (e.g., Branas et al. [34]), there is insufficient work involving the qualitative analysis that might support the development of a unifying grounded theory.

Future studies will have to emphasize the role of confounding variables or package their independent variables using the concept of bundles, an approach borrowed from medicine, in which a variety of variables are clustered to achieve greater efficiency [63]. In this approach, multiple environmental attributes are thought to produce an outcome, although the impact of a single contributor might not be clear.

In this context, we recommend a variety of future studies, including future research directions recommended within the papers included in this literature review:

- Meta-analyses that aggregate data from multiple research projects, empirical and quasi-empirical.
- Studies that focus on the mechanisms that may be impacting behavioral responses [37,53,56,64–66].
- Intervention studies at multiple scales (from small green oases to extensive parks and greenways), particularly those that involve longitudinal pre/post field experiments [11,48,49,55,67,68].
- More studies that exploit the benefits of the development of grounded theory and the gathering of qualitative data, particularly survey and interviews [69].
- More studies that focus specifically on the most violent of crimes—gun violence [11].

4.2. Mediators Contributing to the Relationship Between Greenspace and Violent Crime

As mentioned in the previous section, one of our recommendations involves a more thorough understanding of the mediating variables in the interest of determining causality. We assume that the positive impact of green spaces on crime reduction is attributable to the co-presence of multiple factors that can be divided into physical features (places for community interaction and places for exercise) and qualities (biophilic support, territorial definition, community enfranchisement, and climate moderation; see Figure 2). There are undoubtedly additional factors, but these clusters were most prevalent in the literature and are discussed in the following section.

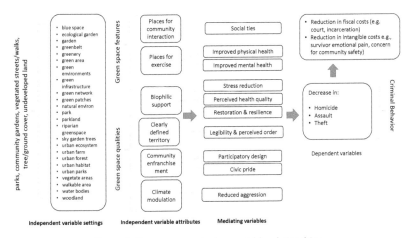

Figure 2. Green space and crime variable relationships.

4.2.1. Places for Community Interaction

Social ties. Outdoor gathering spaces provide the opportunity for interaction among neighborhood members, which increases familiarity and mutual investment in well-being. In keeping with the theory of collective efficacy, greened lots may promote social cohesion and, as a result, the interest in acting for the common good, thereby normalizing healthy behavior in these spaces [70].

Kuo et al. [71] explored the issue of how individuals' natural environments relate to their tendency to establish neighborhood social ties. Their study focused on Chicago public housing units that had direct access to common spaces with varying levels of vegetation. The researchers found a correlation between resident perception of "greenness" and strong neighborhood social ties. In addition, Kuo et al. found that "greenness" of common spaces was associated with perceived neighborhood safety.

With specific regard to children and adolescents, readily visible outdoor recreational spaces provide the opportunity for youth activities and potentially deter gang violence. Researchers have found that the presence of recreational amenities geared toward youth reduces the frequency of criminal activities in this age group [72]. Similarly, playgrounds can provide the opportunity for children to learn social and developmental skills [73], which may help them function more effectively in groups, and ancillary parent interaction has the potential for community adhesion through shared childcare activities.

4.2.2. Places for Exercise

Improved physical health. Parks provide the opportunity for exercise, which may enhance mental acuity [74] and reduce obesity [75]. Improved cognitive skills and health may enhance judgment. Lack of safety, however, may inhibit physical activity and is associated with fear of violence, presence of concerning behaviors, lack of maintenance and good lighting, and the presence of traffic [76]. Han et al. note that gun crimes are associated with long-term negative impacts on health due to reduced use of parks, in addition to the short-term impacts on public safety [77].

Improved mental health. Urban life may be a source of high stress levels [78], and stress and depression are related [79]. The associated mental illness may result in violent behavior. However, exercise is known to produce serotonin and as a result, act as a stress reducer [80]. Parks and other green spaces provide the opportunity for physical activity, including walking, jogging, and playing sports, and, therefore, may contribute to improved mental health.

4.2.3. Biophilic-Related Support

Stress reduction. Nature, in and of itself, may have a calming impact on human psychological and emotional state and cognitive functioning. Higher cortisol levels have been reported in urban areas with a higher percentage of green space [81].

Perceived quality of life. The presence of parks may increase the perceived quality of life [82], particularly as quality of life concerns the provision of perceived choice and control. Reduced lack of choice and control may mitigate the need to strike out against society and engage in violent activities.

Restoration and resilience. Kaplan [83] and others have demonstrated the impact of experience in nature on mental restoration. The resulting ability to make healthier and more productive decisions may be improved by interactions with nature. These interactions may also result in greater resilience [84].

4.2.4. Clearly Defined Territory

Ownership legibility. Clearly defined territories lead to less ambiguity of ownership. Replacement of underdeveloped sites with green spaces is a way to establish territorial markers. The simple act of replacing a run-down, unsupervised lot with a community-developed green space may force sites that previously afforded unhealthy activities to relocated or diminish. The lack of "intrinsic ownership" blurs accountability for maintenance and guardianship [85].

Perceived order. Wilson and Kellings' (1982) theory of "broken windows" suggests that minor cases of disorder create a foundation for more serious crime [86]. This disorder might express itself in the form of visual chaos (garbage, graffiti, abandoned cars) [87]. Several studies associate perceived disorder to physical decline, depression, psychological distress, and perceived powerlessness (e.g., Geis and Ross [88]). The implication is that residents see disorder as an indication of a more problematic neighborhood condition with the potential of compromising health [87]. (The socially controversial underside of this approach is linked to philosophies of crime control that recommend the aggressive arrest of individuals for minor infractions.) At the same time, there is considerable concern around gentrification. Upgrades should be supported and developed by the community and in keeping with local cultural aesthetics [11].

4.2.5. Community Cohesion

Community enfranchisement. Design researchers have known for many years that the participation of users (community members and clients) in the development of guidelines for the physical environment results in greater acceptance of the space and higher levels of maintenance. User participation has been noted for its particular effectiveness in urban settings [89] and provides opportunities for community members to coalesce around common goals. Community cohesion is a primary predictor of reductions in violent crime [90].

Civic pride. Another factor that may contribute to crime reduction is the impact of presence of parks on civic pride [91]; communities that are provided green space amenities may interpret this intervention as an act of respect and collaboration from civic governments. With regard to the duration of exposure, the impact is likely to occur even after short daily interactions with nature [92]. Quality parks may help motivate community members to protect and care for these spaces and reduce the need to erode the physical quality of these facilities as an expression of frustration.

4.2.6. Climate Modulation

Reduced aggression. Among the many ecological benefits of trees and other green features is the reduction of the heat island effect [93]. At the same time, researchers have provided evidence that aggression increases in higher ambient temperatures up to certain levels (i.e., 90 degrees Fahrenheit) [94]. The heat-reducing impact of green space, therefore, may result in reduced crime.

4.3. Limitations

The initial literature search yielded a substantial number of results (14,520 titles reviewed) due to the nature of the language used in the search. Keywords like "green" and "environment" are used broadly outside of the focus topic. To ensure an inclusive set of studies, the researchers relied on manual weeding (title reviews), potentially introducing researcher bias. This will likely continue to be a significant challenge for other researchers seeking to find articles on the topic of violence and green space within such a large collection of literature.

While the search was comprehensive, it was limited to articles written in English and research that took place in the United States. However, corroborating results have been found in other countries, such as Australia and the United Kingdom [92,95]. The researchers were also challenged by the differing definitions of green space and lack of common methods for calibrating green content. We were also unable to incorporate unreported or in-progress studies.

Discerning the impact of confounding variables posed another challenge, particularly in considering the role of maintenance. Beyond the green features of a space, the design and maintenance of a space can also influence its use and perceptions of safety [96]. The presence of green space has the potential to reduce urban crime, but these findings may be substantially moderated by good design and consistent maintenance.

5. Conclusions

Based on the 45 quantitative and qualitative papers summarized here, we can deduce that the presence of parks and other green space reduces urban crime. In the process of our review, we extracted multiple mechanisms from the literature that may account for the impact of green space on crime, including social interaction and recreation, community perception, biophilic stress reduction, climate modulation, and spaces expressing territorial definition. Among the recommendations for future research are a meta-analysis of existing data and the development of grounded theory through qualitative data-gathering methods.

There are several strategies for reducing crime in the U.S. [97], and the provision of green space is one of them. Good public spaces support desirable behaviors and inappropriate public spaces provide the opportunity for increases in criminal behavior, which can be economically costly to society [11,98]. Additionally, safe, accessible green spaces enhance physiological and psychological human health and well-being [99–101]. By providing evidence that access to nature has a mitigating impact on violence in urban settings, city governments and communities are empowered to support these interventions.

Author Contributions: Conceptualization, M.S., N.S. and H.S.; methodology, C.F.; writing—original draft preparation, M.S., K.P.; writing—review and editing, N.S., H.S., K.P., and C.F.; screening and reviewing—N.S., H.S.

Funding: This research received no external funding.

Acknowledgments: The authors would like to acknowledge the contributions of Sabah Mohammed, Department of Design + Environmental Analysis at Cornell University.

Conflicts of Interest: The authors declare no conflict of interest.

Appendix A

Table A1. Literature Review Summary Table.

Paper	Study Location; Time	Sample Size; Units	Predictor: Type of Green	Outcome: Type of Crime
Abu-Lughod (2006) [47]	Highest populated cities in US; 2000	n/a	P	H, A, T
Auchincloss et al. (2019) [55]	Philadelphia, PA; 2009–2014	n/a	V	H, A, T
Blair (2014) [35]	Cincinnati, OH; 1997–2011	5 gardens	G	H, A, T
Blair et al. (2017) [64]	Cincinnati, OH; 2013–2014	12 parks and playgrounds; 10 gardens	P, G	H, A, T
Boessen & Hipp (2018) [67]	Nine US cities; n.d.	109,808 blocks	P	H, A, T
Branas et al. (2011) [40]	Philadelphia, PA; 1999–2008	4436 city lots	G	A, T *
Branas et al. (2016) [11]	Philadelphia, PA; 1999–2008	676 buildings	G	A *
Branas et al. (2018) [34]	Philadelphia, PA; 2011–2013	541 vacant lots	G	A, T *
Brown (2018) [102]	Philadelphia, PA and Detroit, MI; 2011–2015	384 and 297 crimes	P	H, A, T
Burley (2018) [65]	Portland, OR; 2011–2015	93 neighborhoods	V	H, A, T
Crewe (2001) [58]	Boston, MA; 1996-1998	2 neighborhoods	V	A, T
Culyba et al. (2016) [41]	Philadelphia, PA; 2008–2014	143 crimes	P, G	H
DeMotto & Davies (2006) [42]	Kansas City, KS; 2002	40 parks	P	H, A *

Table A1. *Cont.*

Paper	Study Location; Time	Sample Size; Units	Predictor: Type of Green	Outcome: Type of Crime
Deng (2015) [68]	Milwaukee, WI; 2005–2010	1 city	T	A, T
Donahue (2011) [59]	New York, NY; 2001–2008	59 NYC communities (and 200+ other cities)	T	H, A, T
Donovan & Prestemon (2012) [103]	Portland, OR; 2005–2007	2813 households	T	A, T
Garvin et al. (2013) [36]	Philadelphia, PA; 2011	21 lots	G	A, T *
Gilstad-Hayden et al. (2015) [104]	New Haven, CT; 2008–2012	106 census tracts	T	H, A, T
Gorham et al. (2009) [69]	Houston, TX; 2005	11 community gardens	G	T
Harris, Larson, & Ogletree (2018-B) [56]	Chicago, IL; 2011-2015	138 (Study 1) and 62 (Study 2) census tracts	V	H, A, T
Harris (2018) [57]	Chicago, IL; 2011–2015	(see above)	V	H, A, T
Heinze et al. (2018) [52]	Flint, MI; 2009–2013	216 treated lots	G	H, A, T
Kim & Hipp (2018) [48]	Southern CA; 2010	218 cities	P	A, T
Kondo et al. (2015) [45]	Philadelphia, PA; 2000–2012	238 census tracts	U	H, A, T *
Kondo et al. (2016) [53]	Youngstown, OH; 2010–2014	5126 crimes	G	H, A, T
Kondo et al. (2017-A) [105]	Cincinnati, OH; 2005–2014	307 blocks	T	H, A, T
Kondo et al. (2017-B) [46]	Philadelphia, PA; 2008–2011	309 (Study 1) 135 (Study 2) individual victims	T	A *
Kuo & Sullivan (2001) [12]	Chicago, IL; n.d.	98 apartment buildings	T	H, A, T
Lee (2013) [106]	Chicago, IL; 2010	150 parks	P	H, A, T
Li (2008) [61]	Oakland, CA; 2006–2007	234 neighborhoods	T	H, A, T
Lim (2005) [60]	Dallas, TX; n.d.	1683 blocks	T	H, A, T
Locke et al. (2017) [39]	New Haven, CT; 1996–2007	1193 blocks	V	H, A, T
Luke (2013) [107]	Cleveland, OH; 2012	105 gardeners; 92 non-gardeners; 3 community gardens	G	Safety; sense of community
McCord & Houser (2017) [49]	Philadelphia, PA and Louisville, KY; 2005–2010	307 parks	P	H, A, T
Nitkowski (2017) [108]	Milwaukee, WI; 2013–2015	210 census tracts	P	H, A, T
Sadler et al. (2017) [54]	Flint, MI; 2005–2014	1800 lots	G	H, A, T
Schusler et al. (2018) [66]	Chicago, IL; 2009–2013	801 census tracts	T	H, A, T
Seymour et al. (2010) [109]	Los Angeles, CA; 2007	39 individuals	G	Utilitarian relationships with green alleys
Snelgrove et al. (2004) [110]	Austin, TX; 1995	1170 crimes	T	H, A, T

Table A1. *Cont.*

Paper	Study Location; Time	Sample Size; Units	Predictor: Type of Green	Outcome: Type of Crime
Sparks (2011) [62]	San Antonio, TX; 2003–2006	235 census tracts	U	H, A
Stodolska et al. (2011) [111]	Chicago, IL; 2007	26 crimes	P	Benefits, concerns of parks
Troy et al. (2012) [43]	Baltimore, MD; 2007–2010	1208 census tracts	T	H, T *
Troy et al. (2016) [44]	Baltimore, MD; 2007	999 households	T	H, A, T *
Wilcox et al. (2003) [112]	Seattle, WA; 1989–1990	100 census tracts	G	Impact of parks and playgrounds on crime perceptions
Wolfe & Mennis (2012) [37]	Philadelphia, PA; 2005	363 census tracts	T	A, T

TYPE OF GREEN: [P] Parks (larger than community or neighborhood), [G] Community greening (alleys, urban gardens, small green space, greening vacant lots), [V] Vegetated streets and walkways (elevated trails and street tree planting), [T] Trees and ground cover (grass, tree upgrades), [U] Less developed green areas (stormwater upgrades, croplands, wetlands, natural spaces, diverse landscaping); TYPE OF CRIME: [H] Homicide—General, [A] Assault, Sexual Assault, [T] Theft, Robbery, Burglary, * Specifies gun crimes.

References

1. Dzhambov, A.M.; Dimitrova, D.D.; Dimitrakova, E.D. Association between Residential Greenness and Birth Weight: Systematic Review and Meta-Analysis. *Urban For. Urban Green.* **2014**, *13*, 621–629. [CrossRef]
2. Kuo, M. How Might Contact with Nature Promote Human Health? Promising Mechanisms and a Possible Central Pathway. *Front. Psychol.* **2015**, *6*, 1093. [CrossRef] [PubMed]
3. Weinstein, N.; Przybylski, A.K.; Ryan, R.M. Can Nature Make Us More Caring? Effects of Immersion in Nature on Intrinsic Aspirations and Generosity. *Personal. Soc. Psychol. Bull.* **2009**, *35*, 1315–1329. [CrossRef] [PubMed]
4. Bowler, D.E.; Buyung-Ali, L.; Knight, T.M.; Pullin, A.S. Urban Greening to Cool Towns and Cities: A Systematic Review of the Empirical Evidence. *Landsc. Urban Plan.* **2010**, *97*, 147–155. [CrossRef]
5. Buck, D. *Gardens and Health: Implications for Policy and Practice*; The King's Fund: London, UK, 2016.
6. Kondo, M.C.; Andreyeva, E.; South, E.C.; MacDonald, J.M.; Branas, C.C. Neighborhood Interventions to Reduce Violence. *Annu. Rev. Public Health* **2018**, *39*, 253–271. [CrossRef]
7. McMahan, E.A.; Estes, D. The Effect of Contact with Natural Environments on Positive and Negative Affect: A Meta-Analysis. *J. Posit. Psychol.* **2015**, *10*, 507–519. [CrossRef]
8. Ohly, H.; White, M.P.; Wheeler, B.W.; Bethel, A.; Ukoumunne, O.C.; Nikolaou, V.; Garside, R. Attention Restoration Theory: A Systematic Review of the Attention Restoration Potential of Exposure to Natural Environments. *J. Toxicol. Environ. Health Part B* **2016**, *19*, 305–343. [CrossRef]
9. Wolf, K.; Flora, K.; Housley, E. *Research on the Beneficial Aspects of the Experience of Nature in Cities: A Literature Review*; TKF Foundation: Annapolis, MD, USA, 2012.
10. World Health Organization. *Depression and other Common Mental Health Disorders: Global Health Estimates*; World Health Organization: Geneva, Switzerland, 2017.
11. Branas, C.C.; Kondo, M.C.; Murphy, S.M.; South, E.C.; Polsky, D.; MacDonald, J.M. Urban Blight Remediation as a Cost-Beneficial Solution to Firearm Violence. *Am. J. Public Health* **2016**, *106*, 2158–2164. [CrossRef]
12. Kuo, F.E.; Sullivan, W.C. Environment and Crime in the Inner City—Does Vegetation Reduce Crime? *Environ. Behav.* **2001**, *33*, 343. [CrossRef]
13. Mitchell, R.; Popham, F.E. Effect of Exposure to Natural Environment on Health Inequalities: An Observational Population Study. *Lancet* **2008**, *372*, 1655–1660. [CrossRef]
14. Whall, A.L.; Black, M.E.; Groh, C.J.; Yankou, D.J.; Kupferschmid, B.J.; Foster, N.L. The Effect of Natural Environments Upon Agitation and Aggression in Late Stage Dementia Patients. *Am. J. Alzheimers Dis.* **1997**, *12*, 216–220. [CrossRef]

15. Bogar, S.; Beyer, K.M. Green Space, Violence, and Crime: A Systematic Review. *Trauma Violence Abus.* **2016**, *17*, 160–171. [CrossRef] [PubMed]

16. Mancus, G.C.; Campbell, J. Integrative Review of the Intersection of Green Space and Neighborhood Violence. *J. Nurs. Scholarsh.* **2018**, *50*, 117–125. [CrossRef] [PubMed]

17. Arksey, H.; O'Malley, L. Scoping Studies: Towards a Methodological Framework. *Int. J. Soc. Res. Methodol.* **2005**, *8*, 19–32. [CrossRef]

18. Pham, M.T.; Rajić, A.; Greig, J.D.; Sargeant, J.M.; Papadopoulos, A.; Mcewen, S.A. A Scoping Review of Scoping Reviews: Advancing the Approach and Enhancing the Consistency. *Res. Synth. Methods* **2014**, *5*, 371–385. [CrossRef]

19. Federal Bureau of Investigation. 2016 Crime in the United States. Available online: https://ucr.fbi.gov/crime-in-the-u.s/2016/crime-in-the-u.s.-2016/tables/table-1 (accessed on 9 December 2017).

20. Grinshteyn, E.; Hemenway, D. Violent Death Rates: The US Compared with Other High-Income OECD Countries, 2010. *Am. J. Med.* **2016**, *129*, 266–273. [CrossRef]

21. Kochanek, K.D.; Murphy, S.L.; Xu, J.; Arias, E. *Deaths: Final Data for 2017*; National Vital Statistics Reports; National Center for Health Statistics: Hyattsville, MD, USA, 2019.

22. Duwe, G. The Patterns and Prevalence of Mass Public Shootings in the United States, 1915–2013. In *The Wiley Handbook of the Psychology of Mass Shootings*; Wilson, L.C., Ed.; Wiley-Blackwell: Hoboken, NJ, USA, 2016; pp. 20–35.

23. Pati, D.; Lorusso, L.N. How to Write a Systematic Review of the Literature. *HERD Health Environ. Res. Des. J.* **2018**, *11*, 15–30. [CrossRef]

24. Taylor, L.; Hochuli, D.F. Defining Greenspace: Multiple Uses Across Multiple Disciplines. *Landsc. Urban Plan.* **2016**, *158*, 25–38. [CrossRef]

25. Almanza, E.; Jerrett, M.; Dunton, G.; Seto, E.; Pentz, M.A. A Study of Community Design, Greenness, and Physical Activity in Children Using Satellite, GPS and Accelerometer Data. *Health Place* **2012**, *18*, 46–54. [CrossRef]

26. Tavernia, B.G.; Reed, J.M. Spatial Extent and Habitat Context Influence the Nature and Strength of Relationships Between Urbanization Measures. *Landsc. Urban Plan.* **2009**, *92*, 47–52. [CrossRef]

27. Aydin, M.B.S.; Cukur, D. Maintaining the Carbon-Oxygen Balance in Residential Areas: A Method Proposal for Land Use Planning. *Urban For. Urban Green.* **2012**, *11*, 87–94. [CrossRef]

28. Gentin, S. Outdoor Recreation and Ethnicity in Europe: A Review. *Urban For. Urban Green.* **2011**, *10*, 153–161. [CrossRef]

29. Boone-Heinonen, J.; Casanova, K.; Richardson, A.S.; Gordon-Larsen, P. Where Can They Play? Outdoor Spaces and Physical Activity among Adolescents in US Urbanized Areas. *Prev. Med.* **2010**, *51*, 295–298. [CrossRef] [PubMed]

30. Heckert, M. Access and Equity in Greenspace Provision: A Comparison of Methods to Assess the Impacts of Greening Vacant Land. *Trans. GIS* **2013**, *17*, 808–827. [CrossRef]

31. US Environmental Protection Agency. What Is Open Space/Green Space? Available online: https://www3.epa.gov/region1/eco/uep/openspace.html (accessed on 16 October 2019).

32. Federal Bureau of Investigation. 2013 Crime in the United States. Available online: https://ucr.fbi.gov/crime-in-the-u.s/2013/crime-in-the-u.s.-2013/violent-crime/violent-crime-topic-page/violentcrimemain_final (accessed on 16 October 2019).

33. Moher, D.; Liberati, A.; Tetzlaff, J.; Altman, D.G. Preferred Reporting Items for Systematic Reviews and Meta-Analyses: The PRISMA Statement. *Ann. Intern. Med.* **2009**, *151*, 264–269. [CrossRef]

34. Branas, C.C.; South, E.; Kondo, M.C.; Hohl, B.C.; Bourgois, P.; Wiebe, D.J.; Macdonald, J.M. Citywide Cluster Randomized Trial to Restore Blighted Vacant Land and Its Effects on Violence, Crime, and Fear. *Proc. Natl. Acad. Sci. USA* **2018**, *115*, 2946–2951. [CrossRef]

35. Blair, L. Community Gardens and Crime: Exploring the Roles of Criminal Opportunity and Informal Social Control. Ph.D. Thesis, University of Cincinnati, Cincinnati, OH, USA, 2014.

36. Garvin, E.C.; Cannuscio, C.C.; Branas, C.C. Greening Vacant Lots to Reduce Violent Crime: A Randomised Controlled Trial. *Inj. Prev.* **2013**, *19*, 198–203. [CrossRef]

37. Wolfe, M.K.; Mennis, J. Does Vegetation Encourage or Suppress Urban Crime? Evidence from Philadelphia, PA. *Landsc. Urban Plan.* **2012**, *108*, 112–122. [CrossRef]

38. Baumer, E.P.; Lauritsen, J.L. Reporting Crime to the Police, 1973–2005: A Multivariate Analysis of Long-Term Trends in the National Crime Survey (NCS) and National Crime Victimization Survey (NEVS). *Criminology* **2010**, *48*, 131–185. [CrossRef]

39. Locke, D.H.; Han, S.; Kondo, M.C.; Murphy-Dunning, C.; Cox, M. Did Community Greening Reduce Crime? Evidence from New Haven, CT, 1996–2007. *Landsc. Urban Plan.* **2017**, *161*, 72–79. [CrossRef]

40. Branas, C.C.; Cheney, R.A.; Macdonald, J.M.; Tam, V.W.; Jackson, T.D.; Have, T.R.T. A Difference-in-Differences Analysis of Health, Safety, and Greening Vacant Urban Space. *Am. J. Epidemiol.* **2011**, *174*, 1296–1306. [CrossRef] [PubMed]

41. Culyba, A.J.; Jacoby, S.F.; Richmond, T.S.; Fein, J.A.; Hohl, B.C.; Branas, C.C. Modifiable Neighborhood Features Associated with Adolescent Homicide. *JAMA Pediatr.* **2016**, *170*, 473. [CrossRef] [PubMed]

42. Demotto, N.; Davies, C.P. A GIS Analysis of the Relationship between Criminal Offenses and Parks in Kansas City, Kansas. *Cartogr. Geogr. Inf. Sci.* **2006**, *33*, 141–157. [CrossRef]

43. Troy, A.; Grove, J.M.; O'Neil-Dunne, J. The Relationship between Tree Canopy and Crime Rates Across an Urban-rural Gradient in the Greater Baltimore Region. *Landsc. Urban Plan.* **2012**, *106*, 262–270. [CrossRef]

44. Troy, A.; Nunery, A.; Grove, J.M. The Relationship between Residential Yard Management and Neighborhood Crime: An Analysis from Baltimore City and County. *Landsc. Urban Plan.* **2016**, *147*, 78–87. [CrossRef]

45. Kondo, M.C.; Low, S.C.; Henning, J.; Branas, C.C. The Impact of Green Stormwater Infrastructure Installation on Surrounding Health and Safety. *Am. J. Public Health* **2015**, *105*, e114–e121. [CrossRef]

46. Kondo, M.C.; South, E.C.; Branas, C.C.; Richmond, T.S.; Wiebe, D.J. The Association Between Urban Tree Cover and Gun Assault: A Case-Control and Case-Crossover Study. *Am. J. Epidemiol.* **2017**, *186*, 289–296. [CrossRef]

47. Abu-Lughod, R.A. Planning for Crime Reduction: Analysis of Social, Economic, and Physical Variables on United States Cities. Ph.D. Thesis, The University of Texas at Arlington, Arlington, TX, USA, 2006.

48. Kim, Y.-A.; Hipp, J.R. Physical Boundaries and City Boundaries: Consequences for Crime Patterns on Street Segments? *Crime Delinq.* **2018**, *64*, 227–254. [CrossRef]

49. McCord, E.S.; Houser, K. Neighborhood Parks, Evidence of Guardianship, and Crime in Two Diverse US Cities. *Secur. J.* **2017**, *30*, 807–824. [CrossRef]

50. Jacobs, J. *The Death and Life of Great American Cities*; Vintage Books: New York, NY, USA, 1961.

51. Jeffrey, C.R. *Crime Prevention Through Environmental Design*; Sage: Beverly Hills, CA, USA, 1971.

52. Heinze, J.E.; Krusky-Morey, A.; Vagi, K.J.; Reischl, T.M.; Franzen, S.; Pruett, N.K.; Cunningham, R.M.; Zimmerman, M.A. Busy Streets Theory: The Effects of Community-Engaged Greening on Violence. *Am. J. Community Psychol.* **2018**, *62*, 101–109. [CrossRef]

53. Kondo, M.; Hohl, B.; Han, S.; Branas, C. Effects of Greening and Community Reuse of Vacant Lots on Crime. *Urban Stud.* **2016**, *53*, 3279–3295. [CrossRef] [PubMed]

54. Sadler, R.C.; Pizarro, J.; Turchan, B.; Gasteyer, S.P.; McGarrell, E.F. Exploring the Spatial-Temporal Relationships between a Community Greening Program and Neighborhood Rates of Crime. *Appl. Geogr.* **2017**, *83*, 13–26. [CrossRef]

55. Auchincloss, A.H.; Michael, Y.L.; Kuder, J.F.; Shi, J.; Khan, S.; Ballester, L.S. Changes in Physical Activity after Building a Greenway in a Disadvantaged Urban Community: A Natural Experiment. *Prev. Med. Rep.* **2019**, *15*, 100941. [CrossRef] [PubMed]

56. Harris, B.; Larson, L.; Ogletree, S. Different Views from the 606: Examining the Impacts of an Urban Greenway on Crime in Chicago. *Environ. Behav.* **2018**, *50*, 56–85. [CrossRef]

57. Harris, B. The Invisible Walls of the 606: An Examination of the Relationship between an Urban Greenway and Community Change. Ph.D. Thesis, Clemson University, Clemson, SC, USA, 2018.

58. Crewe, K. Linear Parks and Urban Neighbourhoods: A Study of the Crime Impact of the Boston South-West Corridor. *J. Urban Des.* **2001**, *6*, 245–264. [CrossRef]

59. Donahue, J.D. An Empirical Analysis of the Relationships between Tree Cover, Air Quality, and Crime in Urban Areas. Master's Thesis, Georgetown University, Washington, DC, USA, 2011.

60. Lim, J. The Moderating Effects of Vegetation on Human Violent Behavior Caused by Environmental Stressors. Master's Thesis, The University of Texas at Arlington, Arlington, TX, USA, 2005.

61. Li, W. Understand the Social Impact of Green—Evaluation of the Impacts of Urban Vegetation on Neighborhood Crime. Ph.D. Thesis, University of California, Berkeley, CA, USA, 2008.

62. Sparks, C.S. Violent Crime in San Antonio, Texas: An Application of Spatial Epidemiological Methods. *Spat. Spatio-Temporal Epidemiol.* **2011**, *2*, 301–309. [CrossRef]
63. Hamilton, D.K. Can Bundles Be Effective for Both Clinical and Design Interventions? *HERD* **2010**, *3*, 14–18. [CrossRef]
64. Blair, L.; Wilcox, P.; Eck, J. Facilities, Opportunity, and Crime: An Exploratory Analysis of Places in Two Urban Neighborhoods. *Crime Prev. Community Saf.* **2017**, *19*, 61–81. [CrossRef]
65. Burley, B.A. Green Infrastructure and Violence: Do New Street Trees Mitigate Violent Crime? *Health Place* **2018**, *54*, 43–49. [CrossRef]
66. Schusler, T.; Weiss, L.; Treering, D.; Balderama, E. Research Note: Examining the Association between Tree Canopy, Parks and Crime in Chicago. *Landsc. Urban Plan.* **2018**, *170*, 309–313. [CrossRef]
67. Boessen, A.; Hipp, J.R. Parks as Crime Inhibitors or Generators: Examining Parks and the Role of Their Nearby Context. *Soc. Sci. Res.* **2018**, *76*, 186–201. [CrossRef] [PubMed]
68. Deng, C. Integrating Multi-Source Remotely Sensed Datasets to Examine the Impact of Tree Height and Pattern Information on Crimes in Milwaukee, Wisconsin. *Appl. Geogr.* **2015**, *65*, 38–48. [CrossRef]
69. Gorham, M.R.; Waliczek, T.M.; Snelgrove, A.; Zajicek, J.M. The Impact of Community Gardens on Numbers of Property Crimes in Urban Houston. *HortTechnology* **2009**, *19*, 291–296. [CrossRef]
70. Moyer, R.; MacDonald, J.M.; Ridgeway, G.; Branas, C.C. Effect of Remediating Blighted Vacant Land on Shootings: A Citywide Cluster Randomized Trial. *Am. J. Public Health* **2019**, *109*, 140–144. [CrossRef] [PubMed]
71. Kuo, F.E.; Sullivan, W.C.; Coley, R.L.; Brunson, L. Fertile Ground for Community: Inner-City Neighborhood Common Spaces. *Am. J. Community Psychol.* **1998**, *26*, 823–851. [CrossRef]
72. Mendel, R.A. *Prevention or Pork? A Hard-Headed Look at Youth-Oriented Anti-Crime Programs*; 1-887031-50-2; American Youth Policy Forum: Washington, DC, USA, 1995.
73. Fjørtoft, I. The Natural Environment as a Playground for Children: The Impact of Outdoor Play Activities in Pre-Primary School Children. *Early Child. Educ. J.* **2001**, *29*, 111–117. [CrossRef]
74. Hawkins, N.; Anderson, R. The Effects of Exercise on Cognitive Functioning Among the Elderly. *TCA J.* **1996**, *24*, 18–26. [CrossRef]
75. Wolch, J.; Jerrett, M.; Reynolds, K.; McConnell, R.; Chang, R.; Dahmann, N.; Brady, K.; Gilliland, F.; Su, J.G.; Berhane, K. Childhood Obesity and Proximity to Urban Parks and Recreational Resources: A Longitudinal Cohort Study. *Health Place* **2011**, *17*, 207–214. [CrossRef]
76. Groshong, L.; Wilhelm Stanis, S.A.; Kaczynski, A.T.; Hipp, J.A. Attitudes about Perceived Park Safety Among Residents in Low-Income and High Minority Kansas City, Missouri, Neighborhoods. *Environ. Behav.* **2018**. [CrossRef]
77. Han, B.; Cohen, D.A.; Derose, K.P.; Li, J.; Williamson, S. Violent crime and park use in low-income urban neighborhoods. *Am. J. Prev. Med.* **2018**, *54*, 352–358. [CrossRef]
78. Lederbogen, F.; Kirsch, P.; Haddad, L.; Streit, F.; Tost, H.; Schuch, P.; Wüst, S.; Pruessner, J.C.; Rietschel, M.; Deuschle, M.; et al. City Living and Urban Upbringing Affect Neural Social Stress Processing in Humans. *Nature* **2011**, *474*, 498–501. [CrossRef] [PubMed]
79. Lee, W.H.; Kim, C.J. The Relationship between Depression, Perceived Stress, Fatigue and Anger in Clinical Nurses. *J. Korean Acad. Nurs.* **2006**, *36*, 925–932. [CrossRef] [PubMed]
80. Greenwood, B.N.; Fleshner, M. Exercise, Stress Resistance, and Central Serotonergic Systems. *Exerc. Sport Sci. Rev.* **2011**, *39*, 140–149. [CrossRef] [PubMed]
81. Roe, J.J.; Thompson, C.W.; Aspinall, P.A.; Brewer, M.J.; Duff, E.I.; Miller, D.; Mitchell, R.; Clow, A. Green Space and Stress: Evidence from Cortisol Measures in Deprived Urban Communities. *Int. J. Environ. Res. Public Health* **2013**, *10*, 4086–4103. [CrossRef]
82. De Sousa, C.A. Unearthing the Benefits of Brownfield to Green Space Projects: An Examination of Project Use and Quality of Life Impacts. *Local Environ.* **2006**, *11*, 577–600. [CrossRef]
83. Kaplan, S. The Restorative Benefits of Nature: Toward an Integrative Framework. *J. Environ. Psychol.* **1995**, *15*, 169–182. [CrossRef]
84. Wells, N.M.; Evans, G.W. Nearby Nature: A Buffer of Life Stress among Rural Children. *Environ. Behav.* **2003**, *35*, 311–330. [CrossRef]
85. Groff, E.; McCord, E.S. The Role of Neighborhood Parks as Crime Generators. *Secur. J.* **2012**, *25*, 1–24. [CrossRef]

86. Wilson, J.Q.; Kelling, G. The Police and Neighborhood Safety: Broken Windows. 1982. Available online: https://media4.manhattan-institute.org/pdf/_atlantic_monthly-broken_windows.pdf (accessed on 14 December 2019).
87. Sampson, R.J.; Raudenbush, S.W. Seeing Disorder: Neighborhood Stigma and the Social Construction of "Broken Windows". *Soc. Psychol. Q.* **2004**, *67*, 319–342. [CrossRef]
88. Geis, K.J.; Ross, C.E. A New Look at Urban Alienation: The Effect of Neighborhood Disorder on Perceived Powerlessness. *Soc. Psychol. Q.* **1998**, *61*, 232–246. [CrossRef]
89. Sanoff, H. Multiple Views of Participatory Design. *Int. J. Archit. Res. ArchNet-IJAR* **2008**, *2*, 57–69. [CrossRef]
90. Taylor, R.B.; Haberman, C.P.; Groff, E.R. Urban Park Crime: Neighborhood Context and Park Features. *J. Crim. Justice* **2019**, *64*, 101622. [CrossRef]
91. Sadler, R.C.; Pruett, N.K. Mitigating Blight and Building Community Pride in a Legacy City: Lessons Learned from a Land Bank's Clean and Green Programme. *Community Dev. J.* **2017**, *52*, 591–610. [CrossRef]
92. Weinstein, N.; Balmford, A.; DeHaan, C.R.; Gladwell, V.; Bradbury, R.B.; Amano, T. Seeing Community for the Trees: The Links among Contact with Natural Environments, Community Cohesion, and Crime. *BioScience* **2015**, *65*, 1141–1153. [CrossRef]
93. Declet-Barreto, J.; Brazel, A.J.; Martin, C.A.; Chow, W.T.L.; Harlan, S.L. Creating the Park Cool Island in an Inner-City Neighborhood: Heat Mitigation Strategy for Phoenix, AZ. *Urban Ecosyst.* **2013**, *16*, 617–635. [CrossRef]
94. Gamble, J.L.; Hess, J.J. Temperature and Violent Crime in Dallas, Texas: Relationships and Implications of Climate Change. *West. J. Emerg. Med.* **2012**, *13*, 239–246. [CrossRef]
95. Kimpton, A.; Corcoran, J.; Wickes, R. Greenspace and Crime: An Analysis of Greenspace Types, Neighboring Composition, and the Temporal Dimensions of Crime. *J. Res. Crime Delinq.* **2017**, *54*, 303–337. [CrossRef]
96. Hilborn, J. *Dealing with Crime and Disorder in Urban Parks*; US Department of Justice, Office of Community Oriented Policing Services: Washington, DC, USA, 2009.
97. Everytown for Gun Safety; Mayors Against Illegal Guns; National Urban League. Strategies for Reducing Gun Violence in American Cities. Available online: https://everytownresearch.org/reports/strategies-for-reducing-gun-violence-in-american-cities/ (accessed on 13 December 2019).
98. Heaton, P. *Hidden in Plain Sight: What Cost-of-Crime Research Can Tell Us about Investing in Police*; RAND: Santa Monica, CA, USA, 2010.
99. Bratman, G.N.; Anderson, C.B.; Berman, M.G.; Cochran, B.; de Vries, S.; Flanders, J.; Folke, C.; Frumkin, H.; Gross, J.J.; Hartig, T.; et al. Nature and Mental Health: An Ecosystem Service Perspective. *Sci. Adv.* **2019**, *5*, eaax0903. [CrossRef]
100. Frumkin, H.; Bratman, G.N.; Breslow, S.J.; Cochran, B.; Kahn, P.H., Jr.; Lawler, J.J.; Levin, P.S.; Tandon, P.S.; Varanasi, U.; Wolf, K.L.; et al. Nature Contact and Human Health: A Research Agenda. *Environ. Health Perspect.* **2017**, *125*, 075001. [CrossRef]
101. Wolf, K.L.; Measells, M.K.; Grado, S.C.; Robbins, A.S.T. Economic Values of Metro Nature Health Benefits: A Life Course Approach. *Urban For. Urban Green.* **2015**, *14*, 694–701. [CrossRef]
102. Brown, C.L. The Built Environment and Crime: A Comparative Study of Detroit and Philadelphia. Master's Thesis, University of Delaware, Newark, DE, USA, 2018.
103. Donovan, G.H.; Prestemon, J.P. The Effect of Trees on Crime in Portland, Oregon. *Environ. Behav.* **2012**, *44*, 3–30. [CrossRef]
104. Gilstad-Hayden, K.; Wallace, L.R.; Carroll-Scott, A.; Meyer, S.R.; Barbo, S.; Murphy-Dunning, C.; Ickovics, J.R. Research Note: Greater Tree Canopy Cover Is Associated with Lower Rates of Both Violent and Property Crime in New Haven, CT. *Landsc. Urban Plan.* **2015**, *143*, 248–253. [CrossRef]
105. Kondo, M.C.; Han, S.; Donovan, G.H.; MacDonald, J.M. The Association between Urban Trees and Crime: Evidence from the Spread of the Emerald Ash Borer in Cincinnati. *Landsc. Urban Plan.* **2017**, *157*, 193–199. [CrossRef]
106. Lee, S. Does Context Matter? Understanding the Urban Design Requirements of Successful Neighborhood Parks. Ph.D. Thesis, Arizona State University, Tempe, AZ, USA, 2013.
107. Luke, J.A. Urban Community Gardens in a Shrinking City: Community Strength and the Urban Community Gardens of Cleveland, Ohio. Master's Thesis, Kent State University, Kent, OH, USA, 2013.
108. Nitkowski, J. Physical Environment and Crime in Milwaukee Neighborhoods. Master's Thesis, University of Wisconsin-Milwaukee, Milwaukee, WI, USA, 2017.

109. Seymour, M.; Wolch, J.; Reynolds, K.D.; Bradbury, H. Resident Perceptions of Urban Alleys and Alley Greening. *Appl. Geogr.* **2010**, *30*, 380–393. [CrossRef]

110. Snelgrove, A.G.; Michael, J.H.; Waliczek, T.M.; Zajicek, J.M. Urban Greening and Criminal Behavior: A Geographic Information System Perspective. *HortTechnology* **2004**, *14*, 48–51. [CrossRef]

111. Stodolska, M.; Shinew, K.J.; Acevedo, J.C.; Izenstark, D. Perceptions of Urban Parks as Havens and Contested Terrains by Mexican-Americans in Chicago Neighborhoods. *Leis. Sci.* **2011**, *33*, 103–126. [CrossRef]

112. Wilcox, P.; Quisenberry, N.; Jones, S. The Built Environment and Community Crime Risk Interpretation. *J. Res. Crime Delinq.* **2003**, *40*, 322–345. [CrossRef]

International Journal of
*Environmental Research
and Public Health*

Article

Relation between Psychological Restorativeness and Lifestyle, Quality of Life, Resilience, and Stress-Coping in Forest Settings

Norimasa Takayama [1,*], Takeshi Morikawa [1] and Ernest Bielinis [2]

[1] Forestry and Forest Products Research Institute, Forest Research and Management Organization, Matsunosato, Tsukuba, Ibaraki 305-8687, Japan; tmori@ffpri.affrc.go.jp
[2] Department of Forestry and Forest Ecology, Faculty of Environmental Management and Agriculture, University of Warmia and Mazury, Pl. Łódzki 2, 10-727 Olsztyn, Poland; ernest.bielinis@uwm.edu.pl
* Correspondence: hanri@ffpri.affrc.go.jp; Tel.: +81-29-829-8316

Received: 16 February 2019; Accepted: 12 April 2019; Published: 24 April 2019

Abstract: Previous research has mainly dealt with the physiological and psychological restorative effects of the forest environment. However, comparatively few studies have focused on how the traits and attributes of individuals (individual traits) affect the restorative effects of the forest environment. In this study, we examined the relationships between the psychological restorative effects offered by perceived restorativeness of outdoor settings and the individual traits. Then, we investigated the relationships between the restorative indicators that are useful in examining the restorative properties (i.e., the Perceived Restorativeness Scale (PRS); seven indicators in total), the psychological restorative effect (Profile of Mood States (POMS), Restorative Outcome Scale (ROS), positive and negative affect schedule (PANAS), and Subjective Vitality Scale (SVS); 10 indicators in total), and the individual trait indicators that could be used to investigate individual traits (Development of Health and Life Habit Inventory for lifestyle, Lazarus-type Stress Coping Inventory for stress coping, World Health Organization Quality of Life Assessment 26 for quality of life (QOL), and Sukemune-Hiew Resilience test for resilience; 28 indicators in total) in forest and urban settings. Respondents consisted of 46 male students in their twenties. A short-term experiment was conducted using the same method in both environmental settings. We then analyzed the intrinsic restorative properties and the restorative effects of the settings and referred to prior research to determine the restorative effects. Furthermore, we analyzed the relationship between the restorative indicators and the individual trait indicators by correlation analysis and multiple regression (step-wise) analysis. These new findings were obtained: (1) the forest setting was a restorative environment with a higher restorative effect than the urban setting; (2) although the forest setting had a higher restorative effect than the urban setting, and the influence of individual traits was small; (3) in the forest setting, the relationship between the restorative indicators and individual traits indicators were arranged; (4) distancing (Stress coping), psychological health (QOL), and satisfaction with living environment (QOL) were likely important indicators that are related to the restorative effects in the forest setting.

Keywords: lifestyle; mood states; perceived restorativeness scale; positive and negative affect schedule; quality of life; resilience; restorative outcome scale; Shinrin-yoku; stress coping; subjective vitality scale

1. Introduction

With urban life in the modern world, people experience many stressors, which increasingly drive them to seek some form of stress reduction. In the recently urbanized environments and societies, chronic and intense stress, and a deficiency in restoration from stress are well recognized as increasing problems that have long-term negative effects on health [1–3]. Poor stress management is related to psychological issues, such as depression, panic disorder, and burnout syndrome; as well as physical problems, such as neurological, cardiovascular, immunological, and gastroenterological diseases [4,5].

Due to the social problems caused by urban stress, there is an increasing focus on the potentially restorative effects of the natural environment. Lots of evidence on the positive effect of the natural environment on health and happiness has already been published. As a principle, the physiologist Miyazaki advocated using Miyazaki's Nature Therapy Theory to improve health, which was based on an evolutionary anthropological perspective [6]. For example, many studies have considered the physiological effects. One such study compared the physiological effects of walking in and viewing a forest versus a control (i.e., mainly urban) area. It showed that physiological parameters, such as the pulse rate and diastolic blood pressure, were lower for the forest than the urban [7]. Some other studies contributed by having walking and viewing in reverse order [8–10]. Haluza et al. [11] investigated the restorative effect of the physical environment. According to the authors, numerous works concluded that the natural environment is better at reducing stress than the urban environments (where most people live their daily lives) by promoting physical well-being (i.e., lower blood pressure, lower muscle tension, higher skin conductance, higher brain activity, etc. [12–17]). Kühn et al. [18] investigated the associations between geographical properties and brain functioning in terms of brain activity. They found that living near a forest was associated with a healthier amygdala, and suggested that people who lived near the forest would be happier than those who lived away from it.

The Attention Restoration Theory (ART) proposed by Kaplan and Kaplan (1989) [19] help elucidate why natural and forest environments are beneficial to psychological health. Roe and Aspinall [20] examined the psychological recovery effect on psychiatric patients and reported that taking walks in a rural area benefited the affective restoration and cognitive restoration, particularly for people with poor mental health. In addition, some studies on environmental designs made use of these beneficial effects. Ulrich [21] suggested that in hospitals, surgical patients assigned to rooms with windows facing natural scenery (including trees) had shorter post-operative hospital stays, had fewer negative comments from the nurses, and required fewer potent analgesics than those assigned to similar rooms but with windows facing a brick wall. Besides, Velarde et al. [22] indicated that natural environments, including urban parks and several types of forests, were strongly associated with higher energy levels and had other positive health effects in contrast to the urban environment. Recently, some studies reported that the Multiple Mood Scale-Short Form (MMS) scores were higher for friendliness and well-being on days spent walking in the forest compared with the control days. This was especially true among individuals who felt chronic mental stress [23,24]. The MMS score for depression and State-Trait Anxiety Inventory (STAI) [25] score were also lower on the forest days [26]. The psychological responses were also measured by the profile of mood states (POMS) [7,9,27], Zuckerman inventory of personal reactions (ZIPPERS) [28], restorative outcome scales (ROS) [29–31], subjective vitality scale (SVS) [32], and positive and negative affect schedule (PANAS) [33,34]. All indicators showed that the forest setting has more positive psychological restorative effects than the urban setting.

It has been previously mentioned that there may be influences from inter-individual differences on the restorative effect of forest bathing. For example, using on-site experiments, Koyama et al. [35] found that even where users experienced the same forest environment, there were individual differences in how they experienced the environment and the restorative effect obtained. There is a possibility that the health-restoring effects of the forest do not equally benefit all users. This has not yet been explored in specific details; however, Takayama et al. [36] indicated that individual trait differences can act as filters when interpreting the forest setting. The differences were first generated from how the user selects the primary stimulus (e.g., visual) from the forest setting, then also in the quality and degree of the restorative effects obtained from the time spent in the forest. Previous studies that investigated the effects of individual traits on the restorative effects of forests only considered values on personality [36–38], self-efficacy [36,37,39], living environment [36,37], preference and experience [36,37]. Because the factors that people find to be healing differs among individuals, and how the mind and body are restored is a very personal phenomenon. As a result, the possibility that individual traits can influence the restorative effects could not be ruled out. Also, Kaltenborn et al. [40] mentioned that it is necessary to design environments with consideration for the diversity of individuals and specific groups (e.g., culture and/or preference, and so on).

We also agree that it is desirable to provide the most effective choice in consideration of the user's traits, even in future studies aiming to further demonstrate the health and recreational benefits of the forest environment. Therefore, in this study, to clarify whether individual traits affect the restorative effects of the forest setting and to elucidate which indicators of individual traits affect the restorative effects, we attempt to identify the properties of the forest setting that are considered to have high restorative effects using prior research. Then, we also discuss the relationships between the representative individual traits and the restorative effects of the forest setting.

2. Materials and Methods

2.1. Research Sites

The experiments were carried out in four municipalities. The characteristics of each municipality, forest, and urban sites are presented in Table 1. Four forest sites and four urban sites were selected. The urban sites were located near the forest sites. Specific details on the locations of the sites are presented in Figure 1. The urban setting was used as control. The sites were chosen from the area where the respondents reside, as the area should be familiar to the respondents. Our method of site selection for the urban setting was commonly used in other similar studies [7–10,17,41–43]. Using this site selection method should make our results comparable with those of prior studies. The forested sites of Kamiichi (A) and Yoshino (B) are artificial plantations consisting mainly of coniferous trees (i.e., Japanese cedar). Akiota (C) and Oita (D) consist of deciduous forests (i.e., Japanese oak, Sawtooth oak, and others). These forest areas were well-managed, had high levels of lighting, and were relatively flat. The urban sites were located mainly around the downtown major traffic routes, or near the main train station in each municipality. The total experimental period, average number and age of respondents, average temperature and humidity values, and weather conditions throughout the experiment in each site of the four municipalities are presented in Table 2.

Table 1. Summary of the locations of the four municipalities in this study.

Symbol	A	B	C	D
Municipality	Toyama Prefecture Kamiichi Town	Nara Prefecture Yoshino Town	Hiroshima Prefecture Akiota Town	Oita Prefecture Oita city
Forest Site	Temple Pillar Approach in Tateyama Mountain	Trailhead at Yoshino Mountain	West Trail in Shin'nyuzan	Forest Road in Oita Prefectural Forest
Urban Site (Control)	Road before City Center	Road before Kintetsu Department Store	Road before Hiroshima Prefectural Government Building	Road before Oita Bank, Ltd.

Table 2. Summary of the number of respondents and weather conditions at the four study municipalities (A–D).

Symbol	Experimental Period	Number of Respondents	Age of Respondents	Weather Forest/Control	Temperature (°C) Forest/Control (Average ± S.D.)	Humidity (%) Forest/Control (Average ± S.D.)
A	September 6–7, 2011	11	21.4 ± 1.3	Fine/Fine	25.2 ± 1.49/27.5 ± 0.89	52.0 ± 8.46/41.5 ± 2.83
B	August 3–4, 2011	12	21.2 ± 0.8	Fine/Fine	28.4 ± 2.42/34.5 ± 2.80	64.9 ± 12.9/42.6 ± 8.46
C	August 8–9, 2011	12	20.8 ± 1.5	Fine/Fine	26.6 ± 1.29/34.6 ± 1.44	78.0 ± 6.72/56.6 ± 4.26
D	September 13–14, 2011	11	21.1 ± 1.4	Fine/Fine	28.0 ± 1.80/31.8 ± 0.88	63.2 ± 7.09/59.1 ± 2.52

Temperature and humidity were measured every 10 minutes from 9:00 to 16:00 during the experimental period. There were a total of 42 measurements for each parameter.

Figure 1. Location of the four study municipalities in Japan (**A–D**).

2.2. Respondents

We controlled for the variation between respondents to avoid the influence of differences in attributes, such as age or gender, by selecting 46 young male undergraduate and graduate university students as respondents (Table 2). We asked the municipalities' staff at each research site to recruit respondents from the universities nearby. The respondents were not familiar with the study and the underlying theory, as they belonged to a variety of other faculties. By excluding students from the related academic field (e.g., environmental management), academic field-specific bias was avoided. The students were hired by the authors as a research subject over the experimental period. None of the respondents had reported any history of physical or psychiatric disorders. The experiments were conducted in accordance with the Declaration of Helsinki. The research protocol was approved by the Ethics Committee of the Forestry and Forest Products Research Institute in Japan (22FFPRI-1884). All respondents were fully informed of the aims and procedures of this experiment. Their informed consent was obtained prior to the experiment.

2.3. Experimental Schedule

The experiment was conducted over a period of 2 days. The respondents were gathered at a meeting point on the morning of the first day. They were then taken to the meeting room for an orientation where they received an explanation of the experimental procedures. They were required to sign a consent form. After the orientation, the respondents were randomly divided into two groups, each with five to six respondents. On the first day, the respondents in one of the groups were taken to the forest sites, while the respondents in another group were taken to the urban sites. On the second day, the same respondents were taken to the other opposite setting (i.e., forest group into the urban site, and vice versa) to avoid order bias. In a waiting room, we administered four questionnaires, α, β, γ, and δ (Figure 2). These were prepared for each site to investigate the respondents' individual traits (first day only). After which, we requested answers to the four questionnaires (1 to 4; both days) to investigate the baseline before spending time in each setting. After submitting the questionnaires, the respondents were instructed to leave the waiting room and walk a course independently for about 15 minutes for each setting (i.e., walking). Upon returning to the waiting room, they were given a short break and were instructed to sit alone on a chair placed in a representative location within each setting for 15 minutes (i.e., viewing). After viewing, to investigate the restorative effect and restorative properties of each setting, we sat the respondents down and again asked them to complete the same questionnaire (1 to 4), plus questionnaire 5.

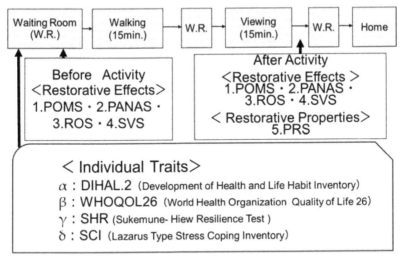

Figure 2. Experimental protocol of the study.

2.4. Measurement

In this study, we tested the hypothesis that the traits of each individual had an influence on the restorative effects received from both settings. As a part of investigating the restorative effects of the forest and the urban setting, it is also important to investigate the restorative properties via the perception of the respondents. Thus, we compared the perception of the respondents with the results obtained from the restorative properties. We measured the data based on three categories: the restorative property of environment (i.e., restorative properties), the restorative effect from the environment (i.e., restorative effects), and the personality traits (i.e., individual traits).

2.4.1. Measurement and Comparison of the Restorative Properties

We used the Perceived Restorativeness Scale (PRS) and requested all respondents to complete the questionnaire to investigate the restorative properties of the forest and urban settings. The PRS was developed by Hartig [44] and was modified based on Kaplan and Kaplan's ART [19]. The Japanese version of the PRS was directly translated by Shibata et al. [45]. It is comprised of 26 items measured based on 11-point Likert scales (Table 3). The theory by Kaplan et al. [19] has four elements of restorative properties: "Being away," "Fascination," "Extent," and "Compatibility." However, the PRS consists of seven elements including the different from ART's elements. In particular, the "Extent" element was further divided into "Coherence" and "Scope" elements. The PRS additionally measures "Familiarity" and "Preference." The extent to which a particular environment restores mental alertness can be measured by including the elements "Being away," "Fascination," "Coherence," "Scope," "Compatibility," "Familiarity," and "Preference."

Table 3. Outline of the questionnaires used in the study.

Name and Abbreviation of Questionnaire	Target of Measurement	Outline of Questionnaire	Before Experiment (B.E.)	After Experiment (A.E.)
Perceived Restorativeness Scale (PRS) *Restorative properties*	Evaluation of restorative properties	7 indicators; Being away, Fascination, Coherence, Extent, Compatibility, Familiarity, Preference	-	O
Profile of Mood States (POMS) *Mood states*	Evaluation of restorative effects	6 indicators; T-A: tension-anxiety, D-D: depression-dejection, A-H: anger-hostility, V: vigor, F: fatigue, C: confusion	O	O
Positive and Negative Affect Schedule (PNANS) *Emotional affects*		2 indicators; Positive affect, Negative affect	O	O
Restorative Outcome Scale (ROS) *Restorativeness*		1 indicator; Subjective restorativeness	O	O
Subjective Vitality Scale (SVS) *Vitality*		1 indicator; Subjective vitality	O	O
Development of Health and Life Habit Inventory (DIHAL.2) *Health and life habit*	Evaluation of individual traits	5 indicators; Health, Exercise, Meal, Rest, Lifestyle habits (Exercise + Meal + Rest)	O	-
WHO Quality of Life 26 (WHOQOL26) *QOL*		5 indicators; Physical health, Psychological health, Social relations, Environment, Total	O	-
Sukemune-Hiew Resilience Test (SHR) *Resilience*		8 indicators; Social support, Self-efficacy, Sociality, Total amount, I: Active (extrinsic)–Active (intrinsic), II: Passive (extrinsic)–Active (intrinsic), III: Active (extrinsic)–Passive (intrinsic), IV: Passive (extrinsic)–Passive (intrinsic)	O	-
Lazarus Type Stress Coping Inventory (SCI) *Stress coping*		10 indicators; Problem-focused coping, Emotion-focused coping, Planful problem solving, Confrontive coping, Seeking social support, Accepting responsibility, Self-controlling, Escape-avoidance, Distancing, Positive reappraisal	O	-

O: Measured point; -: Not measured.

2.4.2. Measurement and Comparison of the Restorative Effects

The POMS is a well-established, analytically-derived factor-based measure of psychological distress. Its validity and reliability are well documented [46]. We used the Japanese version of POMS (covering 65 queries) [47] and its raw data for statistical analysis. The PANAS [33,34] measures the positive and the negative affect through the use of 20 items (10 each for positive and negative affect). We used the Japanese version of the PANAS (covering 16 items; 8 of positive and negative affect each) [48]. The ROS can be used to investigate the restorative emotional and cognitive outcomes in a given environment using the six items. The ROS is based on previous measurements and findings regarding restorative outcomes [29–31]. We used the Japanese version of the ROS (covering all six items) [49]. There are currently two versions of the SVS. One of the versions assesses the enduring traits of individuals. The scale is positively related to self-actualization and self-esteem and is negatively related to depression and anxiety. The other version assesses the state of subjective vitality rather than the enduring aspect. The versions have four items in common and seven items that are different. The reliability and validity of the SVS were confirmed in previous studies [32,50]. In this experiment, we used the four common items to generate a Japanese version of the SVS questionnaire [51]. These four questionnaires have already been used previously in Takayama et al. [41] and Bielinis et al. [42]; therefore, the psychological restorative effect is verifiable from a composite viewpoint (Table 3).

2.4.3. Measurement and Comparison of Individual Traits

In some cases, it was difficult to distinguish between traits and attributes from the indicators of the individual traits consisting of the four items. Here it was not critical to distinguish between these in a strict sense; therefore, we interpreted the meanings of the individual traits more broadly. Even if the original meaning of the term contained elements of the attribute, we defined the term in relation to the individual traits. Our investigation focused on four major psychological aspects: health and lifestyle habits, quality of life, stress coping, and resilience (Table 3). The usefulness of the four aspects was outlined by Li et al. [13,43], who discussed the potential differences in the effects of forest bathing depending on the lifestyle habits of individuals. Takayama et al. [52,53] also investigated the effects of forest bathing on Quality of Life (QOL) [52], resilience, and stress coping [53]. We then referred these to the individual traits considered important. To assess the health and lifestyle habits, we used the Japanese version of the DIHAL.2 (Development of Health and Life Habit Inventory) that was developed by Tokunaga [54]. The questionnaire was developed to diagnose problems in health and lifestyles and to provide a reference point for health guidance. It comprises each of the five indicators: health, exercise, meal, rest, and lifestyle habits. QOL indicates the quality of the activities in a person's life and the quality of life from the perspective of society. It is based on observing how a person can live and be independent, or find happiness. In the present study, the Japanese version of the WHOQOL 26 (World Health Organization Quality of Life Assessment 26) [55] was used to assess the QOL of the respondents. WHOQOL 26 uses five indicators: physical health, psychological health, social relationships, the quality of an environment, and the result of a comprehensive evaluation (Total). Stress coping refers to the process of perceiving stress and adapting to it [56]. To investigate the respondents' stress coping abilities, we used the Lazarus-type stress coping inventory (SCI) questionnaire. The SCI measures the respondents' stress coping abilities using 10 indicators [57]. The test can allocate two strategies and eight approach types. In contrast to stress coping, resilience refers to an individual's ability to adapt one's life activities in the wake of a disadvantageous environment, which could involve family, relationships, health problems, and social risk advantage in the workplace [58]. The Sukemune-Hiew Resilience test (SHR) was used to investigate resilience. The SHR includes the eight indicators allocated to Part 1 and Part 2 of the questionnaire. In Part 1, the questionnaire measures resilience using four factors. Part 2 is concerned with the extrinsic-oriented attitude (represented by action) and the intrinsic-oriented attitude (represented by thinking). We can investigate the four patterns: I: Active (extrinsic)–Active (intrinsic), II: Passive (extrinsic)–Active (intrinsic), III: Active (extrinsic)–Passive (intrinsic), and IV: Passive (extrinsic)–Passive (intrinsic), which are divided into active and passive combinations [59].

2.5. Analysis

After categorizing the survey results of the PRS, we compared the restorative effects between the forest and urban settings for each of the seven indicators mentioned above. We used paired t-test and Bonferroni's correction to avoid Type-I errors (Table 4). The results for individual traits for each indicator were tabulated (Table 5). To compare the restorative effects, we reorganized the part of data used in Takayama et al. [41] and used a paired t-test for each indicator. We compared the scores obtained from each setting before and after staying (Table 6), and the scores from before and after time spent in each setting (Table 7). Subsequently, to investigate the basic trends in the relationship between restorative effects and individual traits, correlation analysis was performed in each of the urban and forest settings. Although correlation analysis could occasionally reveal that the relationship was not only potentially influenced by other factors (possibility of multiple collinearities) but also consisted of type-I; error (statistical reliability), the authors considered it an effective method for grasping the general relationship between the two factors, while acknowledging its limitations. Correlation analyses (uncorrelated tests) were performed for all indicators of individual traits and the restorative effects of each environmental setting to elucidate the overall trends (Tables 8 and 9). Also, to eliminate the influence of other factors as much as possible and to investigate which restorative effects and individual traits were strongly related, we referred to prior research and investigated an effective method for exploring the relationships among multiple factors [60,61]. Therefore, to investigate the relationship from a different perspective using correlation analysis, we attempted to use multiple regression analysis (step-wise, forward selection) with indicators of restorative effects as dependent variables and indicators of individual traits as independent variables (Table 10). The statistical analyses were carried out in IBM SPSS Statistics 25 (IBM).

Table 4. Results from the comparison of the restorative properties between the forest and control sites (n = 46).

	Setting	Being away	Fascination	Coherence	Scope	Compatibility	Familiarity	Preference
Ave.	Forest	34.5	32	22.4	27.5	28.2	3.4	10.9
	Urban (Control)	20.8	27.1	21.2	18.8	23.5	5.4	7.7
S.D.	Forest	12.5	9.8	7	9.2	8	2.9	4.7
	Urban (Control)	13.6	10.3	8.7	8.6	6.6	2.7	4.1
p value		0.000	0.033	0.101	0.000	0.003	0.001	0.001
Significance		**	-	-	**	*	**	**
effect size: r		0.568	0.335	0.204	0.610	0.441	0.487	0.519
statistical power: β		0.975	0.910	0.148	0.993	0.922	0.853	0.952

Ave. = Average; S.D. = Standard Deviation; p values from paired t-test (After applying Bonferroni's correction). Paired t-test significance levels: ** $p < 0.00143$, * $p < 0.00714$, - $p > 0.00714$.

Table 5. Summary results from different questionnaires for assessing individual traits (n = 46).

Health and Life Habit

	Health	Exercise	Meal	Rest	Life Habit
Ave.	41.4	28.6	39.1	42.9	110.6
S.D.	6.49	5.86	8.17	7.56	17.52

Resilience

	Social support	Self-efficacy	Sociality	Total
Ave.	47.2	34.8	16.6	98.7
S.D.	7.92	6.88	3.97	14.99

	Active (extrinsic)-Active (intrinsic)	Passive (extrinsic)-Active (intrinsic)	Active (extrinsic)-Passive (intrinsic)	Passive (extrinsic)-Passive (intrinsic)
Ave.	3.2	2.6	1.4	0.8
S.D.	1.78	1.34	1.19	1.06

Stress Coping

	Planful	Confront	Seeking social support	Accepting responsibility	Self-control
Ave.	8.2	6.7	4.7	8.6	7.3
S.D.	3.94	2.90	3.48	3.86	3.16

	Escape	Distancing	Positive reappraisal	Problem-focused	Emotion-focused
Ave.	5.7	6.7	8.4	30.0	26.2
S.D.	2.60	3.25	4.12	12.55	8.73

Quality of Life

	Physical health	Psychological health	Social relationships	Environment	Total
Ave.	25.1	20.2	10.4	26.3	6.4
S.D.	3.69	3.85	2.31	4.06	1.58

Table 6. The results of the comparison between the forest and urban (control) settings in terms of the restorative effect (n = 46).

		POMS						PANAS		ROS	SVS
		T-A	D-D	A-H	V	F	C	Negative	Positive		
Before	Ave.(S.D.) Forest	43.15 (8.03)	44.00 (5.61)	41.89 (7.46)	42.78 (10.39)	43.83 (9.31)	44.13 (8.37)	11.96 (6.22)	22.00 (9.61)	4.36 (0.95)	12.37 (4.76)
	Urban (Control)	42.39 (8.22)	43.52 (6.37)	40.33 (6.43)	41.41 (9.28)	44.87 (9.47)	43.87 (7.04)	14.20 (8.44)	20.59 (9.61)	4.19 (1.07)	11.54 (4.29)
	p value	0.451	0.449	0.161	0.322	0.410	0.780	0.079	0.282	0.345	0.237
	Significance	-	-	-	-	-	-	-	-	-	-
	effect size: r	0.113	0.114	0.208	0.148	0.124	0.042	0.259	0.161	0.141	0.176
	statistical power: β	0.115	0.117	0.285	0.165	0.128	0.059	0.406	0.186	0.149	0.218
After	Ave.(S.D.) Forest	39.15 (5.97)	42.37 (4.97)	39.63 (4.51)	45.15 (9.61)	42.7 (9.25)	40.93 (5.84)	11.76 (6.11)	23.93 (9.98)	4.93 (1.09)	13.22 (4.75)
	Urban (Control)	43.98 (7.58)	43.63 (5.52)	40.96 (4.83)	36.35 (8.62)	49.54 (10.22)	45.61 (7.86)	16.26 (8.32)	21.39 (10.29)	3.52 (1.49)	9.74 (5.47)
	p value	0.000	0.059	0.038	0.000	0.000	0.000	0.001	0.047	0.000	0.001
	Significance	**	-	-	**	**	**	*	-	**	*
	effect size: r	0.586	0.278	0.304	0.729	0.591	0.519	0.460	0.291	0.576	0.469
	statistical power: β	0.997	0.475	0.556	1.000	0.998	0.979	0.925	0.513	0.996	0.936

Ave. = Average; S.D. = Standard Deviation; POMS = Profile of Mood States; PANAS = Positive and Negative Affect Schedule; ROS = Restorative Outcame Scale; SVS = Subjective Vitality Scale. Paired t-test (After applying Bonferroni's correction): ** p < 0.001 * p = 0.005 - p > 0.005. Takayama et al. (2014) [41] was referred to and cited to arrange this table.

Table 7. Results of comparison between the before and after staying in terms of restorative effect (n = 46).

		POMS						PANAS		ROS	SVS
		T-A	D-D	A-H	V	F	C	Negative	Positive		
Forest	Before Ave.(S.D.)	43.15 (8.03)	44 (5.61)	41.89 (7.46)	42.78 (10.39)	43.83 (9.31)	44.13 (8.37)	11.96 (6.22)	22 (9.55)	4.36 (0.95)	12.37 (4.76)
	After Ave.(S.D.)	39.15 (5.97)	42.37 (4.97)	39.63 (4.51)	45.15 (9.61)	42.70 (9.25)	40.93 (5.84)	11.76 (6.11)	23.93 (9.98)	4.93 (1.09)	13.22 (4.75)
	p value	0.001	0.006	0.026	0.115	0.322	0.009	0.199	0.851	0.414	0.000
	Significance	*	-	-	-	-	-	-	-	-	**
	effect size: r	0.485	0.395	0.324	0.233	0.148	0.378	0.191	0.029	0.122	0.58
	statistical power: β	0.953	0.804	0.613	0.349	0.165	0.764	0.054	0.507	0.930	0.269
Urban(Control)	Before Ave.(S.D.)	42.39 (8.22)	43.52 (6.37)	40.33 (6.43)	41.41 (9.28)	44.87 (9.47)	43.87 (7.04)	14.20 (8.44)	20.59 (9.61)	4.19 (1.07)	11.54 (4.29)
	After Ave.(S.D.)	43.98 (7.58)	43.63 (5.52)	40.96 (4.83)	36.35 (8.62)	49.54 (10.22)	45.61 (7.86)	16.26 (8.32)	21.39 (10.29)	3.52 (1.49)	9.74 (5.47)
	p value	0.001	0.025	0.858	0.049	0.091	0.57	0.001	0.002	0.718	0.002
	Significance	*	-	-	-	-	-	*	*	-	*
	effect size: r	0.295	0.205	0.216	0.589	0.504	0.316	0.291	0.080	0.430	0.426
	statistical power: β	0.494	0.275	0.297	0.969	0.900	0.545	0.468	0.081	0.796	0.796

Ave. = Average; S.D. = Standard Deviation. Paired t-test (after applying Bonferroni's correction): ** $p < 0.001$, * $p < 0.005$, - $p > 0.005$. Takayama et al. (2014) [41] was referred to and cited to arrange this table.

Table 8. Results from correlation analyses in the forest setting (n = 46).

		POMS						PANAS		ROS	SVS
		T–A	D–D	A–H	V	F	C	Positive	Negative		
Health and Life habit	Health	0.031	-0.023	-0.068	0.168	-0.051	-0.046	-0.122	0.202	0.216	-0.168
	Exercise	-0.026	0.054	0.080	0.066	0.158	0.085	-0.071	0.093	0.175	-0.097
	Meal	-0.283	-0.184	0.217	0.239	-0.182	-0.295 *	-0.107	-0.023	0.141	-0.009
	Rest	-0.107	-0.103	0.153	0.274	-0.122	-0.213	-0.142	0.006	0.067	-0.110
	Life habit	-0.186	-0.117	0.196	0.255	-0.093	-0.200	-0.133	0.025	0.156	-0.085
Stress coping	Planful	0.032	0.063	0.003	0.041	-0.074	-0.061	-0.069	-0.068	0.013	-0.210
	Confront	0.143	0.114	0.063	-0.274	-0.004	0.114	0.100	0.005	-0.130	-0.181
	Seeking social support	0.053	0.114	0.179	0.082	0.149	0.024	-0.052	0.116	0.036	-0.201
	Accepting responsibility	0.253	0.114	-0.017	-0.024	-0.126	-0.067	0.095	0.106	-0.008	-0.181
	Self–control	-0.078	-0.030	-0.135	-0.010	-0.138	-0.147	-0.105	0.168	0.232	-0.271
	Escape	0.086	0.140	-0.003	-0.221	0.109	0.059	-0.012	0.191	-0.023	-0.223
	Distancing	0.062	0.185	-0.070	-0.338 *	0.069	0.223	0.032	-0.028	-0.210	-0.339 *
	Positive reappraisal	0.053	0.137	-0.093	-0.019	-0.224	-0.041	-0.132	0.143	0.092	-0.075
	Problem–focused	0.081	0.140	-0.005	0.006	-0.128	-0.080	-0.045	0.059	0.045	-0.234
	Emotion–focused	0.117	0.185	-0.028	-0.260	0.046	0.124	0.001	0.142	-0.039	-0.303 *
Resilience	Social support	-0.072	0.051	-0.097	0.072	-0.054	-0.130	-0.084	0.118	0.069	-0.166
	Self–efficacy	-0.056	-0.077	0.033	0.082	-0.207	-0.175	-0.153	0.064	0.044	-0.201
	Sociality	-0.006	-0.128	-0.066	0.022	0.123	-0.097	-0.246	-0.095	-0.030	-0.272
	Total	-0.066	-0.035	-0.054	0.082	-0.091	-0.175	-0.180	0.067	0.049	-0.252
	Active(extrinsic)–Active(intrinsic)	-0.015	0.105	-0.111	-0.045	-0.183	-0.077	0.037	-0.138	-0.160	-0.147
	Passive(extrinsic)–Active(intrinsic)	0.044	-0.042	-0.042	-0.062	0.205	0.245	-0.055	0.105	0.077	0.015
	Active(extrinsic)–Passive(intrinsic)	-0.050	-0.048	0.250	0.170	0.022	-0.078	-0.112	-0.067	0.157	0.039
	Passive(extrinsic)–Passive(intrinsic)	0.025	-0.065	-0.041	-0.038	0.022	-0.093	0.133	0.176	-0.005	0.184
Quality of life (QOL)	Physical health	0.024	-0.069	0.069	0.230	0.008	-0.028	-0.195	0.146	0.208	-0.201
	Psychological health	0.067	0.035	-0.071	-0.041	-0.015	0.003	0.069	0.012	0.159	-0.365 *
	Social relationships	0.068	0.029	-0.054	0.055	-0.014	-0.111	0.039	0.056	0.206	-0.286
	Environment	-0.228	-0.182	0.007	0.195	-0.334 *	-0.335 *	-0.115	0.073	0.207	-0.080
	Total	-0.083	-0.024	0.084	0.148	0.026	-0.107	-0.143	0.034	0.138	-0.221

Test for no correlation (Pearson's correlation): * p < 0.05.

Table 9. Results from correlation analyses in the urban (control) setting (n = 46).

		POMS						PANAS		ROS	SVS
		T–A	D–D	A–H	V	F	C	Positive	Negative		
Health and Life habit	Health	0.138	0.031	0.002	−0.068	−0.110	−0.095	0.210	0.089	−0.129	0.059
	Exercise	0.124	0.091	0.148	−0.122	0.183	−0.007	0.080	0.161	−0.190	−0.202
	Meal	−0.046	0.142	−0.084	−0.086	−0.338 *	0.129	−0.002	0.087	0.067	0.446 **
	Rest	0.051	0.117	−0.028	−0.026	−0.187	0.075	−0.118	0.212	−0.028	0.249
	Life habit	0.036	0.147	−0.002	−0.091	−0.181	0.090	−0.028	0.188	−0.045	0.253
Stress coping	Playful	0.037	0.047	−0.074	−0.168	−0.327 *	−0.136	0.013	0.048	−0.070	0.266
	Confront	0.119	0.063	−0.084	−0.237	−0.073	−0.149	0.011	0.090	−0.231	−0.016
	Seeking social support	0.275	0.383 **	0.263	−0.085	0.203	0.094	−0.092	0.068	−0.069	−0.160
	Accepting responsibility	0.216	0.235	0.197	−0.152	−0.120	0.003	−0.011	0.238	−0.172	0.131
	Self–control	0.051	0.087	−0.043	−0.346 *	−0.080	−0.251	0.299 *	0.143	−0.444 **	−0.072
	Escape	0.222	0.245	0.013	−0.365 *	0.128	−0.115	0.263	0.076	−0.401 **	−0.211
	Distancing	−0.001	0.011	−0.034	−0.445 **	−0.093	−0.175	0.285	0.003	−0.171	−0.010
	Positive reappraisal	0.189	0.135	0.029	−0.155	−0.200	−0.072	0.010	0.017	−0.247	0.170
	Problem–focused	0.186	0.204	0.061	−0.201	−0.184	−0.058	−0.012	0.127	−0.194	0.162
	Emotion–focused	0.168	0.180	0.032	−0.441 **	−0.013	−0.210	0.283	0.085	−0.400 **	−0.119
Resilience	Social support	0.241	0.221	0.161	−0.015	0.256	0.177	0.140	0.268	−0.089	−0.164
	Self–efficacy	−0.055	0.004	−0.020	−0.025	−0.072	0.022	0.049	0.232	−0.162	0.091
	Sociality	0.169	0.073	−0.019	−0.056	0.047	0.003	0.083	0.215	−0.202	−0.049
	Total	0.147	0.138	0.071	−0.035	0.115	0.104	0.119	0.305 *	−0.175	−0.058
	Active(extrinsic)–Active(intrinsic)	0.008	−0.001	0.006	0.239	−0.068	0.066	−0.143	0.165	0.106	0.115
	Passive(extrinsic)–Active(intrinsic)	−0.059	−0.090	−0.065	−0.179	0.044	−0.181	−0.028	−0.362 *	−0.023	−0.162
	Active(extrinsic)–Passive(intrinsic)	−0.009	0.097	0.049	−0.278	0.048	−0.045	0.302 *	0.245	−0.300 *	−0.080
	Passive(extrinsic)–Passive(intrinsic)	0.071	0.008	0.018	0.137	0.005	0.169	−0.064	−0.095	0.189	0.102
Quality of life (QOL)	Physical health	0.063	0.060	0.060	0.008	−0.073	−0.088	−0.018	0.136	−0.117	0.023
	Psychological health	−0.156	−0.040	0.018	0.070	0.017	−0.163	0.276	0.177	−0.191	−0.122
	Social relationships	0.005	0.056	−0.027	0.128	0.043	−0.062	0.001	0.287	−0.250	−0.085
	Environment	−0.109	0.021	−0.099	−0.072	−0.178	−0.140	0.058	0.310 *	−0.129	0.103
	Total	−0.129	0.025	0.161	0.090	−0.011	−0.025	0.093	0.203	0.068	−0.004

Test for no correlation (Pearson's correlation): ** $p < 0.01$ * $p < 0.05$.

Table 10. Results from multiple regression analysis (step-wise, forward selection; n = 46).

		Forest setting							Urban (Control) setting									
		POMS						SVS	POMS						PANAS		ROS	SVS
		T-A	D-D	A-H	V	F	C		T-A	D-D	A-H	V	F	C	Positive	Negative		
	R²				0.114	0.197	0.112	0.219		0.275	0.114		0.131	0.27		0.147	0.294	0.295
	adjR²				0.094	0.159	0.092	0.182		0.241	0.094		0.111	0.218		0.127	0.261	0.262
	Statistical power-β				0.503	0.597	0.495	0.660		0.787	0.503		0.571	0.659		0.628	0.820	0.822
Health and Life habit	Health												-0.338 *					
	Exercise																	
	Meal																	
	Rest																	
	Life habit																	
Stress coping	Planful																	
	Confront																	
	Seeking social support																	
	Accepting responsibility									0.383 **								
	Self-control																	
	Escape							-0.295 *				-0.468 **				0.597 **	-0.452 **	-0.66 **
	Distancing																	
	Positive reappraisal															-0.413 *		0.365 *
	Problem-focused																	
	Emotion-focused																	
Resilience	Social support																	
	Self-efficacy																	
	Sociality																	
	Total											0.278 *						
	Active(extrinsic)-Active(intrinsic)														-0.362 *			
	Passive(extrinsic)-Active(intrinsic)																	
	Active(extrinsic)-Passive(intrinsic)																	
	Passive(extrinsic)-Passive(intrinsic)															0.285 *	-0.312 *	
Quality of life (QOL)	Physical health					-0.560 **	-.335 *	-0.325 *										
	Psychological health																	
	Social relationships																	
	Environment																	
	Total																	

(1) The numbers are the partial regression coefficient selected as a result of the step-wise method (forward selection). (2) Shaded squares indicate items that were significant in the correlation analysis (Tables 8 and 9). (3) PANAS's and ROS's that had non-significant relationships by the analysis in the forest setting were omitted from the table; ** $p < 0.01$, * $p < 0.05$.

3. Results

3.1. Comparison of Restorative Properties between Forest and Urban Sites

In the comparison between forest and urban sites using the PRS score, significant differences were found in all indicators except for "Fascination" and "Coherence." "Being away," "Scope," "Compatibility" and "Preference" were significantly higher in the forest sites, and only "Familiarity" was significantly higher in the urban sites. As for "Fascination" and "Coherence," there was little difference in the scores among the two different sites and no significant difference between the two sites could be confirmed (Table 4).

3.2. Restorative Effects and Individual Traits

Table 5 summarizes the average values and the standard deviations of the 28 indicators used as measures of individual traits. The results of the restorative effect between the forest and urban site are shown in Table 6. Before spending time in the respective settings, there were no significant differences among sites in any of the restorative effect indicators in terms of the participants' psychological state. In contrast, after spending time in the respective settings, there were significant differences among sites for "T-A, " "V, " "F, " "C" (POMS), "Negative affect" (PANAS), "ROS" and "SVS." A positive psychological restorative effect was observed across sites for the forest setting.

Table 7 shows the results from the psychological measurements before and after staying at each site. In the forest site, "T-A" decreased significantly after staying. In contrast, "SVS" increased after staying. Meanwhile, "SVS" decreased significantly in the urban site, and "T-A" (POMS), "Negative affect," and "Positive affect" increased significantly. Therefore, the results from the forest and urban setting were very different.

3.3. The Relationship between Individual Traits and Restorative Effects

3.3.1. Correlation Analysis

To investigate the overall trend of the relationship between the restorative effects and individual traits for each environmental setting, correlation analyses were performed for all indicators (Tables 8 and 9). The restorative effect index consisted of 10 indicators. Net values were obtained by subtracting the restorative effect obtained before from the values obtained after spending time in the site. The individual traits index, which consists of 28 indicators, was used as the individual traits indicator. In the forest setting, 7 out of 280 correlations were significant (Table 8). In the urban setting, 17 of 280 correlations were significant (Table 9).

3.3.2. Multiple Regression Analysis (Step-Wise)

We conducted multiple regression analyses (step-wise, forward selection) to investigate further how the indicators of individual traits influenced the restorative effect. In the forest setting, there were significant relationships in 5 out of 280 cases. On the other hand, in the urban setting 12 out of 280 relationships were significant. Table 10 presents the results from multiple regression analysis and provides information on the direction of the relationships.

4. Discussion

4.1. The Restorative Properties of Environmental Settings and Restorative Effects

We assessed the restorative properties of the forest and urban settings and the psychological restorative effects. First, the scores related to daily life, Being away, Scope and Compatibility were statistically higher in the forest setting than in the urban setting (Table 4). This result implies that the forest setting has higher restorative properties than the urban setting. The ART of Kaplan and Kaplan [19] indicates that an environment has four functions that can exert beneficial restorative effects: (1) Being away (feeling refreshed away from everyday occurrences), (2) Fascination (that which enthralls people and attracts interest), (3) Extent (which infuses feelings of spatial expanse; divided into Coherence and Scope in the PRS), and (4) Compatibility (which makes the environment feel suitable). From our results, an appropriately managed forest setting could be an excellent restorative environment in comparison with the urban setting, the latter of which is where the majority of people live. On the other hand, in the comparison of the restorative properties to the restorative effects, there was no significant difference between the forest and urban settings for participants in all indicators before spending time in each of the respective settings (Table 6). However, after the respondents have spent time in the forest, they attained a significantly more positive psychological state than after spending time in the urban setting (Table 6), and even before staying at the forest setting (Table 7).

Overall the four forest sites are restorative environments with higher restorative effects in contrast to the four urban sites. The higher psychologically restorative effect may be because of the highly restorative properties of the forest acting as a stimulus to the respondents.

4.2. The Restorative Effects and Individual Traits in the Forest and Urban Settings

4.2.1. Forest Setting

There was a significant correlation between the composite index of the 10 restorative effects and the index of 28 individual traits. More specifically, in the forest setting there were significant correlations between Vigor (POMS) and Distancing (Stress coping), Fatigue (POMS) and Environment (QOL), Confusion (POMS) and Meal (Health and life habit), Confusion (POMS) and Environment (QOL), SVS and Distancing (Stress coping), and Emotion-focused (Stress coping) and Psychological health (QOL; Table 8). In other words, stress coping ability of the "Distancing type" (i.e., thinking that problems are not related to oneself and trying to forget problems and suffering) was inversely correlated with the feeling of liveliness and energy after spending time in the forest. The environmental area of QOL (i.e., a degree of satisfaction with one's living environment on a daily basis) was inversely correlated with fatigue and confusion after spending time in the forest. Since both Vigor (POMS) and SVS are restorative indicators of the psychological state, people who have a relatively low ability to cope with the distancing type of stress (i.e., those who confront themselves without escaping from problems) are more likely to increase in psychological vigor from spending time in the forest setting.

Furthermore, the distancing type of stress coping had a negative relationship with Vigor (POMS; −0.338) and SVS (−0.295). The environmental area of QOL had a negative relationship with Fatigue (POMS; −0.560) and Confusion (POMS; −0.335; Table 10). This suggests that people with distancing characteristics may have a lower psychological state of vigor from staying in a forest setting. People who are satisfied with their daily living environment may also have less fatigue and confusion. These results are reflected in the results of the correlation analyses. Thus, psychological health has a negative relationship with SVS (−0.325). In addition, people dissatisfied with their psychological health aspect of their QOL tended to experience greater effects on subjective vitality.

These results suggest that factors related to lifestyle and resilience do not necessarily affect the effect of staying in a forest setting. Li et al. [13,43] indicated that forest staying is effective for treating lifestyle diseases and Takayama et al. [53] suggested that psychological resilience is improved by staying in a forest. However, if we considered psychological resilience as factors of individual traits, there was a possibility that it did not necessarily affect the effect of a single and short-term forest staying. Some indicators of stress coping and QOL were considered as factors influencing the effect of short-term forest staying. Takayama [36] analyzed the relationship between the big five factors of personality and the restorative effects by forest staying. He hypothesized that only a limited number of factors would have an influence on the effect of forest staying. Our results provide support for their hypothesis.

4.2.2. Urban Setting

The equivalent analysis was carried out with the urban setting as the control (Table 9). There were 17 significant correlations. Some significant correlations were obtained compared with the forest setting (7 cases). In particular, among the individual traits, the indices for stress coping (10 indicators) was significantly correlated with many restorative effect indicators. For example, the self-control, escape, distancing, and emotion-focused types were significantly negatively correlated with Vigor (POMS). In addition, for the passive (extrinsic)–active (intrinsic) type (Resilience), the environmental area (QOL) was significantly correlated with positive emotions (PANAS). Thus, the directions of correlation between individual traits and the restorative indicator were variable.

According to the results from the multiple regression analyses (Table 10), there were 12 significant relationships between individual traits and the restorative indicator. Taking negative emotion (PANAS) as an example, people who are of the self-control type (i.e., stress coping: take countermeasures to deal with stress by self-control; 0.597), and not those who are the problem-focused type (i.e., stress coping: tries to solve problems face to face; −0.413) and the passive (extrinsic)–active (intrinsic) type (i.e., resilience: people whose behavior is active but the way of thinking is passive; 0.285), tended to have negative emotions after spending time in the urban environment. Our results suggest that by staying in the urban setting, people who are of the self-control type and active (extrinsic)–passive (intrinsic) type (i.e., resilience: behavior is passive, but the way of thinking is negative) may experience reduced psychological restoration (ROS). As described above, our results provided details on how individual traits have a significant influence on the restorative effect of spending time in urban areas.

In the urban setting, there were significant influences from the three categories (i.e., lifestyle, stress coping, resilience). In addition, we found that the psychological state was affected by more individual traits from staying in the urban setting than in the forest setting. The urban setting was not a restorative environment compared to the forest, and a restorative effect was not expected either. However, in the urban setting, as a strong stimulus was scattered (in contrast to the forest setting), it was necessary for each person to pay more attention to sufficiently adapt to their environment. For this reason, we considered that many more individual traits were related to the stay in the urban setting rather than in the forest setting.

4.2.3. Comprehensive Discussion

When the results for the forest and urban settings were compared, both correlation and multiple regression analyses revealed many significant relationships in the urban setting (17 for the correlation analysis and 12 for the multiple regression analysis). On the other hand, fewer significant relationships were revealed in the forest setting (7 for the correlation analysis and 5 for the multiple regression analysis). As previously discussed, a forest setting has a higher restorative effect than an urban setting (Tables 6 and 7) because of its higher restorative properties (Table 4), the same as the previous studies [7–10,17,42,43]. Thus, if the same amount of time was spent in both settings, a higher restorative effect should be obtained in the forest setting. Considering that a forest setting has a higher restorative function, the differences in the number of significant relationships that were revealed in this study implies that it is also affected by individual traits, and not simply due to the effect of the environment alone. In other words, the restorative effect obtained in an urban setting tends to be strongly influenced by the individual traits of the respondents. In the forest setting, it is thought that there was a stable restorative effect with little influence from the variation in individual traits. Although there were only a few significant relationships in the forest setting, there were some significant relationships between individual traits and the restorative effect of the environment. How we relate to the environment and feel about the environment varies among individuals. Therefore, as we have revealed, it is important for the forest management and planning, as well as for forest experience programs to consider the knowledge from research on the different effects that spending time in a forest setting have on people with different individual traits [26,36]. For example, if we would like to improve the psychological state of the vigor of a participants' gpoup, we should investigate their stress coping mechanisms in advance and then expose the participants to different distancing type and non-distancing type of environments and programs [53]. We will then be able to provide more effective services. From these findings, it was clear that individual traits (such as the distancing type of stress coping) and the psychological and environmental areas of QOL are related to restorative effects. These have not been dealt with previously. Regarding the effect of individual traits, which not been given much attention in previous studies, on the planning of forest use and management, we believe that more concrete knowledge could be acquired that will enable more effective forest planning, with consideration of individual traits. Takayama [36] showed that during a walk for a short-term in a forest setting alone, the restorative effect of forest staying was high for people who have high neuroticism, and people who have high extroversion had lower effectiveness. Furthermore, it is important to develop a forest bathing program suited for each individual trait type. Since we found that three factors, namely (1) distance from the stressor to protect oneself from stress, (2) satisfaction with daily living environment, and (3) psychological health, were related to the effect of single and short-term forest staying, the results from this study can be considered to use in the arrangement of a new and diversified program.

5. Conclusions

In the present study, we investigated and analyzed the relationships between individual traits (i.e., health and lifestyle, stress coping ability, resilience, and QOL) and the restorative effects from a short stay in a forest setting. The following findings were obtained.

The forest setting is a restorative environment with a higher restorative effect than the urban setting.

Although the forest setting had a higher restorative effect than the urban setting, the influence of differences in individual traits was minimal.

The relationships between restorative indicators of the forest environment and individual traits indicators were elucidated.

Distancing (stress coping), psychological health (QOL), and satisfaction with the living environment (QOL) were potentially important indicators related to the restorative effects in the forest setting.

The above results were obtained even though the time the respondents spent in the forest settings was relatively short. Therefore, regardless of individual traits, people can experience a psychological restorative effect by simply spending time in a forest setting for a relatively short period (approximately 30 minutes to 1 hour). Several studies explored the effects of individual differences on the effect of staying in the forest setting, such as Takayama [36] and Takayama et al. [37]; however, none used the indicators of individual trait types explored herein, where we analyzed the influence of the forest setting compared with the urban setting (control). Therefore, the present study is exploratory. There were numerous indicators of individual traits that could not be accounted for in the present study. Also, the number of respondents was limited due to the use of direct recruitment of students on-site.

Furthermore, we chose young men in their 20s as respondents to control for the respondent's attributes. The effects of gender and age would require further exploration in the future. The relationships between cognitive differences in individual respondents (i.e., restorative properties) and differences in restorative effects between forest and urban settings (i.e., restorative effects), or the relationship between cognitive differences and individual traits have not been studied previously. Exploring such dynamics is important for establishing the overall relationships among individual traits and restorativeness, which should be elucidated further in future studies. Although a well-managed forest environment is highly beneficial to users regardless of individual differences, further research could focus on developing optimal forest management and forest experience programs, while taking into account differences among individual users.

The present study had some limitations. First, with regard to correlation and multiple regression analysis, it may be necessary to consider the potential of the presence of type-I errors. Therefore, readers should be careful when they consider the results of the present study. In addition, the urban setting was used as a control and compared with the forest setting, referring to many previous studies [7–10,12,13,17,27,35–37,39,41–43]. However, the results could vary depending on a researcher's perspective on what should be applied as a control. We would like to see the progress research in this field in the future.

Author Contributions: N.T. participated in experimental design, data acquisition, analysis, interpretation, and drafting of the manuscript. T.M. contributed to give the necessary opinions for collecting experimental data and for writing the manuscript. E.B. conceived of the study and participated in data interpretation, drafting of the manuscript, and general supervision of the research. All authors have read and approved this manuscript.

Funding: This project was supported by the Japan Society for the Promotion of Science.

Acknowledgments: We are grateful to all researchers who obtained the related data and gave the authors numerous ideas and insights. Kalevi Korpela not only gave us information on questionnaires such as ROS and SVS but also guidance on the preparation of this article. We would like to express our appreciation to him. We also appreciate Sato Sanai, who is a doctor candidate at the graduate school of Tsukuba University, for her contributions to the data analysis. Finally, we would like to thank Kazunori Hanyu of Nihon University for giving us a lot of advice on statistical analysis.

Conflicts of Interest: The authors declare no conflict of interest.

References

1. Frumkin, H. Beyond toxicity human health and the natural environment. *Am. J. Prev. Med.* **2001**, *20*, 234–240. [CrossRef]

2. McEwen, B.S. Protective and damaging effects of stress mediators. *N. Engl. J. Med.* **1998**, *338*, 171–179. [CrossRef] [PubMed]

3. Sluiter, J.K.; Frings-Dresen, M.H.W.; Meijman, T.F.; van der Beek, A.J. Reactivity and recovery from different types of work measured by catechol amines and cortisol: A systematic literature overview. *Occup. Environ. Med.* **2000**, *57*, 298–315. [CrossRef] [PubMed]

4. Nilsson, K.; Sangster, M.; Konijnendijk, C.C. Forest, tress and human health and well-being. In *Forest, Trees and Human Health*; Nilsson, K., Sangster, M., Gallis, C., Hartig, T., de Vries, S., Seeland, K., Schipperijn, J., Eds.; Springer: Dordrecht, The Netherlands, 2011; pp. 1–19.

5. Quick, J.C.; Wright, T.A.; Adkins, J.A.; Nelson, D.L.; Quick, J.D. *Preventive Stress Management in Organizations*, 2nd ed.; American Psychological Association: Washington, DC, USA, 2013; ISBN 1-4338-1185-5 (Hardcover); ISBN 978-1-4338-1185-2 (Hardcover).

6. Miyazaki, Y.; Park, B.J.; Lee, J. "Nature therapy," in Designing Our Future. In *Local Perspectives on Bioproduction, Ecosystems and Humanity*; Osaki, M., Braimoh, A., Nakagami, K., Eds.; United Nations University Press: Tokyo, Japan, 2011; pp. 407–412.

7. Park, B.J.; Tsunetsugu, Y.; Kasetani, T.; Morikawa, T.; Kagawa, T.; Miyazaki, Y. Physiological effects of forest recreation in a young conifer forest in Hinokage town, Japan. *Silva Fenn.* **2009**, *43*, 291–301.

8. Park, B.J.; Tsunetsugu, Y.; Kasetani, T.; Kagawa, T.; Miyazaki, Y. The physiological effects of Shinrin-yoku (taking in the forest atmosphere or forest bathing): Evidence from field experiments in 24 forests across Japan. *Environ. Health Prev. Med.* **2010**, *15*, 18–26. [CrossRef]

9. Tsunetsugu, Y.; Park, B.J.; Miyazaki, Y. Trends in research related to "shinrin-yoku" (taking in the forest atmosphere or forest bathing) in Japan. *Environ. Health Prev. Med.* **2010**, *15*, 27–37. [CrossRef] [PubMed]

10. Tyrväinen, L.; Ojala, A.; Korpela, K.; Lanki, T.; Tsunetsugu, Y.; Kagawa, T. The influence of urban green environments on stress relief measures: A field experiment. *J. Environ. Psychol.* **2014**, *38*, 1–9. [CrossRef]

11. Haluza, D.; Schönbauer, R.; Cervinka, R. Green perspectives for public health: A narrative review on the physiological effects of experiencing outdoor nature. *Int. J. Environ. Res. Public Health* **2014**, *11*, 5445–5461. [CrossRef]

12. Li, Q.; Kobayashi, M.; Kawada, T. Relationships between percentage of forest coverage and standardized mortality ratios (SMR) of cancers in all prefectures in Japan. *Open Public Health J.* **2008**, *1*, 1–7. [CrossRef]

13. Li, Q.; Morimoto, K.; Kobayashi, M.; Inagaki, H.; Katsumata, M.; Hirata, Y.; Hirata, K.; Shimizu, T.; Li, Y.J.; Wakayama, Y.; et al. A forest bathing trip increases human natural killer activity and expression of anti-cancer proteins in female subjects. *J. Biol. Regul. Homeost. Agents* **2008**, *22*, 45–55.

14. Laumann, K.; Gärling, T.; Stormark, K.M. Selective attention and heart rate responses to natural and urban environments. *J. Environ. Psychol.* **2003**, *23*, 125–134. [CrossRef]

15. Ohtsuka, Y.; Yabunaka, N.; Takayama, S. Shinrin-yoku (forest-air bathing and walking) effectively decreases blood glucose levels in diabetic patients. *Int. J. Biometeorol.* **1998**, *41*, 125–127. [CrossRef]

16. Ohira, H.; Takagi, S.; Masui, K.; Oishi, M.; Obata, A. Effects on shinrin-yoku (forest-air bathing and walking) on mental and physical health. *Bull. Tokai Women Univ.* **1999**, *19*, 217–232. (In Japanese)
17. Lee, J.; Park, B.-J.J.; Tsunetsugu, Y.; Kagawa, T.; Miyazaki, Y. The restorative effects of viewing real forest landscapes: Based on a comparison with urban landscapes. *Scand. J. For. Res.* **2009**, *24*, 227–234. [CrossRef]
18. Kühn, S.; Düzel, S.; Eibich, P.; Krekel, C.; Wüstemann, H.; Kolbe, J.; Martensson, J.; Goebel, J.; Gallinat, J.; Wagner, G.G.; et al. In search of features that constitute an "enriched environment" in humans: Associations between geographical properties and brain structure. *Sci. Rep.* **2017**, *7*. [CrossRef]
19. Kaplan, R.; Kaplan, S. *The Experience of Nature: A Psychological Perspective, reprint*; Ulrich's Bookstore: Ann Arbor, MI, USA, 1995; pp. 177–200.
20. Roe, J.; Aspinall, P. The restorative benefits of walking in urban and rural setting in adults with good and poor mental health. *Health Place* **2011**, *17*, 103–113. [CrossRef]
21. Ulrich, R.S. View through a window may influence recovery from surgery. *Science* **1984**, *224*, 420–421. [CrossRef]
22. Velarde, M.D.; Fry, G.; Tveit, M. Health effects of viewing landscapes—Landscape types in environmental psychology. *Urban For. Urban Green.* **2007**, *6*, 199–212. [CrossRef]
23. Terasaki, M.; Koga, A.; Kishimoto, Y. Construction of the multiple mood scale short form. In Proceedings of the 55th Annual Conversation of Japanese Psychological Association, Tohoku, Japan, 29–31 October 1991. (In Japanese).
24. Terasaki, M.; Kishimoto, Y.; Koga, A. Construction of a multiple mood scale. *Jpn. J. Psychol.* **1992**, *62*, 350–356. (In Japanese) [CrossRef]
25. Spielberger, C.D.; Gorsuch, R.L.; Lushene, R.E. *STAI Manual for the State-Trait Anxiety Inventory "Self-Evaluation Questionnaire"*; Spielberger, C.D., Gorsuch, R.L., Lushene, R.E., Eds.; Consulting Psychologist Press: Sunnyvale, CA, USA, 1970.
26. Morita, E.; Fukuda, S.; Nagano, J.; Hamajima, N.; Yamamoto, H.; Iwai, Y.; Nakashima, T.; Ohira, H.; Shirakawa, T. Psychological effects of forest environments on healthy adults: Shinrin-yoku (forest-air bathing, walking) as a possible method of stress reduction. *Public Health* **2007**, *121*, 54–63. [CrossRef]
27. Park, B.-J.; Furuya, K.; Kasetani, T.; Takayama, N.; Kagawa, T.; Miyazaki, Y. Relationship between psychological responses and physical environments in forest settings. *Landsc. Urban Plan.* **2011**, *102*. [CrossRef]
28. Hartig, T.; Mang, M.; Evans, G.W. Restorative Effects of Natural Environment Experiences. *Environ. Behav.* **1991**, *23*, 3–26. [CrossRef]
29. Korpela, K.M.; Ylén, M.; Tyrväinen, L.; Silvennoinen, H. Determinants of restorative experiences in everyday favourite places running title: Determinants of everyday restorative experiences. *Health Place* **2007**, *14*, 636–652. [CrossRef]
30. Korpela, K.M.; Ylén, M.; Tyrväinen, L.; Silvennoinen, H. Favorite green, waterside and urban environments, restorative experiences and perceived health in Finland. *Health Promot. Int.* **2010**, *25*, 200–209. [CrossRef]
31. Pasanen, T.; Ojala, A.; Tyrväinen, L.; Korpela, K. Restoration, well-being, and everyday physical activity in indoor, built outdoor and natural outdoor settings. *J. Environ. Psychol.* **2018**, *59*, 85–93. [CrossRef]
32. Ryan, R.M.; Frederick, C.M. On energy, personality and health: Subjective vitality as a dynamic reflection of well-being. *J. Personal.* **1997**, *65*, 529–565. [CrossRef]
33. Watson, D.; Clark, L.A.; Carey, G. Positive and negative affectivity and their relation to anxiety and depressive disorders. *J. Abnorm. Psychol.* **1988**, *97*, 346–353. [CrossRef] [PubMed]
34. Watson, D.; Clark, L.A.; Tellegen, A. Development and validation of brief measures of positive and negative affect: The PANAS Scales. *J. Personal. Soc. Psychol.* **1988**, *47*, 1063–1070. [CrossRef]
35. Koyama, Y.; Takayama, N.; Park, B.-J.; Kagawa, T.; Miyazaki, Y. The Relationship between changes in Salivary Cortisol and the Subjective Impression of Shinrin-yoku (Taking in an Atmosphere of the Forest, or Forest Bathing). *Jpn. J. Physiol. Anthropol.* **2009**, *14*, 21–24. (In Japanese)
36. Takayama, N. *Stress Reduction Effect and Future Development of Shinrin-Yoku Based on Evidence*; Shinkoh Igaku Shuppansha: Tokyo, Japan, 2012; ISBN 9784880027364. (In Japanese)
37. Takayama, N.; Tsutsui, S.; Park, B.-J.; Kasetani, T.; Aramaki, M.; Kagawa, T. The Influence of User's Personality to Evaluate the Images of On-site Forest Environment. *J. Jpn. Inst. Landsc. Archit.* **2010**, *73*, 531–536. (In Japanese) [CrossRef]
38. Song, C.; Ikei, H.; Lee, J.; Park, B.-J.; Kagawa, T.; Miyazaki, Y. Individual differences in the physiological effects of forest therapy based on Type A and Type B behavior patterns. *J. Physiol. Anthropol.* **2013**, *32*, 14. [CrossRef]
39. Takayama, N.; Kagawa, T.; Park, B.-J. Research on the influence of Taking in a forest atmosphere to the self-efficacy of subjects. *Kanto J. For. Res.* **2009**, *60*, 85–86. (In Japanese)

40. Kaltenborn, B.P.; Bjerke, T. Associations between environmental value orientations and landscape preferences. *Landsc. Urban Plan.* **2002**, *59*, 1–11. [CrossRef]

41. Takayama, N.; Korpela, K.; Lee, J.; Morikawa, T.; Tsunetsugu, Y.; Park, B.J.; Li, Q.; Tyrväinen, L.; Miyazaki, Y.; Kagawa, T. Emotional, restorative and vitalizing effects of forest and urban environments at four sites in Japan. *Int. J. Environ. Res. Public Health* **2014**, *11*, 7207–7230. [CrossRef]

42. Bielinis, E.; Takayama, N.; Boiko, S.; Omelan, A.; Bielinis, L. The effect of winter forest bathing on psychological relaxation of young Polish adults. *Urban For. Urban Green.* **2017**, *29*, 276–283. [CrossRef]

43. Li, Q.; Morimoto, K.; Kobayashi, M.; Inagaki, H.; Katsumata, M.; Hirata, Y.; Hirata, K.; Suzuki, H.; Li, Y.; Wakayama, Y.; et al. Visiting a forest, but not a city, increases human natural killer activity and expression of anti-cancer proteins. *Int. J. Immunopathol. Pharmacol.* **2008**, *21*, 117–127. [CrossRef] [PubMed]

44. Hartig, T.; Kaiser, F.G.; Bowler, P.A. *Further Development of a Measure of Perceived Environmental Restorativeness*; Working Paper; Uppsala University: Gävle, Sweden, 1997.

45. Shibata, S.; Hata, T.; Miwa, Y. Perceived Restorativeness Scale (PRS) Translation and Validation of a Japanese Version of the Perceived Restorativeness Scale (PRS). *MERA J.* **2008**, *11*, 1–10. (In Japanese)

46. McNair, D.M.; Lorr, M.M.; McNair, D.; Maurice, L. An analysis of mood in neurotics. *J. Abnorm. Soc. Psychol.* **1964**, *69*, 620–627. [CrossRef]

47. Yokoyama, K.; Araki, S.; Kawakami, N.; Takeshita, T. Production of the Japanese edition of profile of mood states (POMS): Assessment of reliability and validity. *Jpn. J. Public Health* **1990**, *37*, 913–918. (In Japanese)

48. Sato, A.; Yasuda, A. Development of the Japanese version of Positive and Negative Affect Schedule (PANAS) scales. *J. Character Psychol.* **2001**, *9*, 138–139. (In Japanese)

49. Fujisawa, M.; Takayama, N. Verification of Restorative Effect in Off-site Forest Bathing by ROS Japanese Edition. *J. Environ. Inf. Sci.* **2014**, *28*, 316–366. (In Japanese)

50. Ryan, R.M.; Weinstein, N.; Bernstein, J.; Brown, K.W.; Mistretta, L.; Gagne, M.; Gagné, M. Vitalizing effects of being outdoors and in nature. *J. Environ. Psychol.* **2010**, *30*, 159–168. [CrossRef]

51. Takayama, N. Development and Verification on Subjective Vitality Scale of the Japanese Edition (SVS-J). *J. Environ. Inf. Sci.* **2015**, *29*, 33–36. (In Japanese)

52. Takayama, N.; Saito, K.; Fujiwara, A. Continuing Changes in QOL and Mood States Staying in a University Forest Area for Five Days and Four Nights. *J. Jpn. For. Soc.* **2018**, *100*, 71–76. [CrossRef]

53. Takayama, N.; Saito, K.; Fujiwara, A.; Tsutsui, S. Influence of Five-day Suburban Forest Stay on Stress Coping, Resilience, and Mood States. *J. Environ. Inf. Sci.* **2018**, *2017*, 49–57. [CrossRef]

54. Tokunaga, M. Development of Health and Life Habit Inventory (DIHAL.2). *J. Health Sci.* **2005**, *27*, 57–70. (In Japanese)

55. World Health Organization; Tazaki, M.; Nakane, Y. *Guide of WHOQOL 26*, Revised ed.; Kanekoshobo: Tokyo, Japan, 2007. (In Japanese)

56. Kosugi, S.; Shimazu, A.; Tanaka, K.; Tanaka, M.; Taneichi, R.; Hayashi, Y.; Fukukawa, Y.; Yamazaki, K. *Stress Psychology—A Process and Coping of the Individual Difference (In Japanese)*; Kosugi, S., Ed.; Kawashima shoten: Tokyo, Japan, 2002. (In Japanese)

57. Japan Health Psychology Institution. *Manual for Stress Coping Inventory (In Japanese)*; Jitsumukyouiku-Shuppan: Tokyo, Japan, 2007. (In Japanese)

58. Tisseron, S. *Resilience: What Is Restorativeness of the Mind*; Mataichiro, A., Ed.; Hakusuisha: Tokyo, Japan, 2016; ISBN 4560510091. (In Japanese)

59. Sukemune, S. *Guidebook for Sukemune-Hiew Resilience Test*; Takei scientific instruments: Niigata, Japan, 2007. (In Japanese)

60. Kennedy, T.D.; Burnett, K.F.; Edmonds, W.A. Intellectual, behavioral, and personality correlates of violent vs. non-violent juvenile offenders. *Aggress. Behav.* **2011**, *37*, 315–325. [CrossRef]

61. Monteleone, A.M.; Monteleone, P.; Volpe, U.; De Riso, F.; Fico, G.; Giugliano, R.; Nigro, M.; Maj, M. Impaired cortisol awakening response in eating disorder women with childhood trauma exposure: Evidence for a dose-dependent effect of the traumatic load. *Psychol. Med.* **2018**, *48*, 952–960. [CrossRef] [PubMed]

International Journal of
*Environmental Research
and Public Health*

Article

Urban Open Space Is Associated with Better Renal Function of Adult Residents in New Taipei City

Jien-Wen Chien [1,2], Ya-Ru Yang [1], Szu-Ying Chen [3,4], Yu-Jun Chang [5] and Chang-Chuan Chan [1,*]

[1]   Institute of Occupational Medicine and Industrial Hygiene, College of Public Health, National Taiwan University, Taipei 10020, Taiwan
[2]   Department of Pediatric Nephrology, Changhua Christian Children's Hospital, Changhua 50006, Taiwan
[3]   Division of surgical intensive care, Department of critical care, E-Da Hospital, Kaohsiung 82445, Taiwan
[4]   Department of Nursing, Fooyin University, Kaohsiung 83102, Taiwan
[5]   Epidemiology and Biostatistics Center, Changhua Christian Hospital, Changhua 50006, Taiwan
*   Correspondence: ccchan@ntu.edu.tw; Tel.: +886-2-3366-8082

Received: 7 June 2019; Accepted: 4 July 2019; Published: 9 July 2019

Abstract: The purpose of this study is to explore the association between proximity to open space and adult renal function. This was a cross-sectional study. Adult residents of Taipei metropolis were recruited in the analysis. The proximity of each subject to open space was measured using the Geographic Information System. Residents were divided into two groups: with and without chronic kidney disease (CKD). We made univariable comparisons between the two groups. The logistic regression models were used to estimate the odds ratio of CKD. Forest plot was used to examine the effect of interaction between distance to open space and subgroup variable on CKD. A total number of 21,656 subjects with mean age 53.6 years were enrolled in the study. Of the subjects, 2226 (10.28%) had CKD. The mean and standard deviation of distance to open space were 117.23 m and 80.19 m, respectively. Every 100 m distance to open space was associated with an odds ratio of 1.071 for CKD. Subgroup analysis revealed that residents of female, without hypertension, or without impaired fasting glucose (IFG) living more than 200 m from open spaces have greater odds of CKD than those living less than 200 m. Conclusions: Proximity to open space was associated with a lower prevalence of CKD among adults in Taiwan. Such association was enhanced among females and healthy adults without hypertension or impaired fasting glucose (IFG).

Keywords: open spaces 2; CKD 3; renal function

1. Introduction

It is well known that the ecosystem affects the well-being of humankind. However, urbanization is a global trend, especially in Asia. More than half of the world's population currently live in cities [1]. Urban citizens living in artificial environments may lack the services providing by the ecosystem. Fortunately, open spaces can compensate for it. The effects of open space on health include both physiological and psychological benefits. Open space independently augments the physical activity of nearby residents [2]. The urban environmental design may also influence behavior, mental health [3] and well-being [4] of residents. Other health benefits include an increase in birth weight (grams) among the lowest education level group [5], decrease in number of small for gestational age births [6], lower prevalence of early childhood asthma [7], lower morbidity (especially for anxiety disorder and depression) [8], lower mortality (especially for respiratory disease) [9], lower heat-related mortality [10], increase in longevity of urban senior citizens [11], and lower risk of stroke mortality [12].

Studies on the health effects of open space in Asia are relatively fewer. Moreover, to our best knowledge, the association between open space and renal diseases has not been explored. In Taiwan, the prevalence of chronic kidney disease (CKD) among adults ranged from 6.9% [13] to 11.9% [14], exerting a huge burden on the health care system. This study aims to explore the relationship between proximity to open space and renal diseases among adults.

2. Materials and Methods

Study Population: Residents aged 30 and above who lived in metropolitan areas (six districts with population densities higher than 20,000/km^2) in 2009 were the target of the study (Figure 1). One of the districts, Yonghe City, has the highest population density in Taiwan, with population density 41,446/km^2 in 2009. Subjects were recruited from the New Taipei City Health Screening Program from 2007 to 2009. This annual program was supervised by the Department of Health of the New Taipei City Government. All citizens aged 30 and above were invited to participate in the program every three years. Subjects with incomplete information were excluded from the study. Finally, 2630 subjects were excluded due to missing data and a total of 21,656 subjects from six districts were included in this study. Permission to use these decoded data from the Department of Health of the New Taipei City Government was granted. This study was approved by the Joint Institutional Review Boards of National Health Research Institutes (Approval number: EO-104-PP-09).

Figure 1. The map of Taiwan with New Taipei City in gray area (left). Residents lived in the metropolitan area of the city were included in the study (right).

Health Data: The annual health screening program was implemented by the Department of Health of the New Taipei City Government. The program involved a self-reporting questionnaire, interview by a physician, and blood sampling for biochemistry study. Demographic data including age, gender, location of residence, alcohol consumption, smoking, and betel-nut-chewing habit were collected. During the health examination, weight, height, and blood pressure of each subject were measured. Serum creatinine was analyzed using isotope dilution mass spectrometry (IDMS)-traceable method. Hypertension was defined as a systolic blood pressure ≥140 mmHg or a diastolic blood pressure ≥90 mmHg. Overweight was defined as body mass index (BMI) ≥24 (kg/m^2). Impaired fasting glucose (IFG) was defined as fasting sugar ≥126 mg/dL. Hypercholesteremia was defined as serum cholesterol level ≥200 mg/dL.

Urinanalysis: Each subject's first morning mid-void urine was collected during the day of the survey. Urinanalysis was performed using Multistix test strips (Bayer Diarnostics, Victoria, Australia) which grade proteinuria as negative, trace, 1+ (0.3 g/L), 2+ (1 g/L), 3+ (3 g/L) or 4+ (≥20 g/L) by a reaction with tetrabromphenol blue.

Renal Function: To estimate the glomerular filtration rate (GFR), the CKD-EPI-Taiwan equation was used. This equation has been proved to have a lower bias than that derived from the modification of diet in renal disease (MDRD) study [15]. The CKD-EPI-Taiwan equation is as follows: eGFR = 1.262 × [1.41×min(Scr/κ, 1)$^\alpha$ × max(Scr/κ,1)$^{1.209}$ × 0.993^{Age} × 1.018(if female) × 1.159(if black)]$^{0.914}$, where

Scr denotes serum creatinine, κ is 0.7 for female and 0.9 for male, α is −0.329 for female and −0.411 for male, min indicates the minimum of Scr/κ or 1, and max indicates the maximum of Scr/κ or 1. In this study, CKD was defined as eGFR ≤60 mL/min/1.73 m², which stands for 50% loss in renal function.

Distance to Open Space: Locations of subjects' residence were geocoded using the ArcGIS 10.1 software, and their minimum distance to open space was calculated. Open space is defined by the US EPA as any open piece of land that is undeveloped (has no buildings or built structures) and is accessible to the public [16]. Examples of open space are green space, schoolyards, playgrounds, public plazas and vacant lots. The land use database was established by the National Land Surveying and Mapping Center, Taiwan in 2007. According to the standard land use coding manual of the database, open spaces include public utilities (schools, code 00202-0260204) and recreation areas (park, code 070201; playground, code 070202; and sports facility, code 070203) (Figure 2).

Figure 2. Locations of open spaces in the metropolitan area (six districts) of New Taipei City.

Particulate Matter Exposures: We used land use regression (LUR) model to estimate annual average concentrations of $PM_{2.5}$, $PM_{2.5Absorbance}$, PM_{10}, and PM_{Coarse} at each resident's address. The LUR model was developed for the European Study of Cohorts for Air Pollution Effects (ESCAPE) project [17]. To develop the model, we measured the pollutants in 20 different sites during three 14-day periods from October 2009 to August 2010. The detailed protocol of the model was described in the previous paper [18].

Statistical analysis: Patients were divided into two groups according to the level of eGFR: with and without CKD. The demographic data and other clinically relevant data of continuous variables are presented as mean and standard deviation, whereas categorical variables were presented as numbers and percentages. We made univariable statistical comparisons between groups by Student's t-tests for continuous data, and chi-square tests for categorical data. The logistic regression model was used to estimate the odds ratio of CKD. Variables that achieved statistical significance in univariate analysis were subsequently entered into multivariate analysis. According to the distance from the open space, it is divided into two groups of ≥200 meters and <200 meters. Forest plot showing the effect of interaction between distance to open space and subgroup variable (age, gender, overweight, hypertension, impaired fasting glucose (IFG), age, smoking, and drinking) on CKD. The final model retains only statistically significant factors after multiple regression. All data were analyzed using the IBM SPSS Statistics for Windows, Version 22.0 (IBM Corp., Armonk, NY). *p*-values < 0.05 were considered statistically significant.

3. Results

New Taipei City had the most population among Taiwan's administrative regions. The metropolitan area of the city includes six districts, which had population densities range from 20,308/km² to 41,446/km². The six districts had a total area of 924,855 km² and total population of 2,190,426 citizens at the end of 2009. The distribution location of open spaces is shown in Figure 2.

The recreational spaces (include parks, playgrounds and sport venues) had a total area of 6.46 km^2 (6.99%). The school spaces (include elementary schools, high schools, and colleges) had a total area of 3.9km^2 (4.22%). Per capita open space availability is 4.7 m^2.

Table 1 lists the demographic data of our study subjects. In brief, there were 21,656 subjects in total, with a mean age 53.6 years and male to female ratio of 1:2. About half (50.4%) of the subjects were overweight, and 33.2% of subjects were hypertensive. Moreover, 18.3% of subjects had smoked, 36.7% had consumed alcohol, and 3.5% had chewed betel nut. The mean eGFR was 77.05 mL/min/m^2. The prevalence of CKD (eGFR < 60 mL/min/m^2) was 10.3%. The mean ± SD distance to open space was 117.23 ± 80.19 m. The longest distance to open space was 570.7 m.

Table 1. Characteristics of the 21,656 subjects.

Variable	Mean ± SD or N (%)
Age (years)	53.65 ± 10.37
30 ≤ Age < 40	1155 (5.33)
40 ≤ Age < 50	6670 (30.80)
50 ≤ Age < 60	8183 (37.79)
60 ≤ Age < 70	4044 (18.67)
70 ≤ Age < 80	1276 (5.89)
80 ≤ Age < 90	315 (1.45)
90 ≤ Age	13 (0.06)
Female Gender	14,477 (66.85)
Body mass index (BMI) (kg/m^2)	24.35 ± 3.51
Waist (cm)	79.21 ± 9.97
SBP (mm Hg)	128.8 ± 20.16
DBP (mm Hg)	81.8 ± 12.15
Fasting Glucose (mg/dL)	100.61 ± 25.75
Cholesterol (mg/dL)	204.42 ± 36.54
Triglycerides (mg/dL)	118.73 ± 81.49
HDL (mg/dL)	68.96 ± 36.52
LDL (mg/dL)	113.06 ± 41.52
BUN (mg/dL)	13.48 ± 4.36
Creatinine (mg/dL)	0.84 ± 0.31
Hypertension	7164 (33.15)
Overweight	10,902 (50.44)
Impaired fasting glucose (IFG)	1550 (7.16)
Distance to Major Road (meter)	667.96 ± 453.78
Smoking	
Never	17,664 (81.62)
Former	1502 (6.94)
Current Smoker	2477 (11.44)
Alcohol consumption	
Never	13,716 (63.36)
Former	406 (1.88)
Seldom	6430 (29.70)
Current	1095 (5.06)
Ever Chew Betel nut	763 (3.53)
Education level	
Uneducated	1523 (7.09)
Elementary or junior high school	9179 (42.71)
High school	6417 (29.86)
College or graduate school	4371 (20.34)
Estimated Glomerular Filtration Rate (eGFR)	77.05 ± 13.18
Chronic Kidney Disease (CKD)	2226 (10.28)
Distance to Open Space (m)	117.23 ± 80.19
1-year exposure	
PM$_{2.5}$ (μg/m^3)	26.64 ± 5.01
PM$_{2.5Absorbance}$ (10^{-5}/m)	1.94 ± 0.39
PM$_{10}$ (μg/m^3)	49.48 ± 4.13
PM$_{Coarse}$ (μg/m^3)	23.13 ± 3.68

Hypertension defined as SBP ≥ 140 mmHg or DBP ≥ 90 mmHg. Overweight defined as BMI ≥ 24 (kg/m^2). Impaired fasting glucose (IFG) defines as fasting glucose ≥ 126 mg/dL. Alcohol consumption: current defines as drinking on regular bases, seldom defines as drinking only on special occasions, formal defines as quitted from drinking on regular bases previously estimated glomerular filtration rate (eGFR) estimated by equation of chronic kidney disease (CKD)-EPI-Taiwan. CKD defined as eGFR ≤ 60 mL/min per 1.73 m^2.

Study subjects were divided into two groups according to the level of eGFR: with and without CKD. We made univariable statistical comparisons between groups by Student's t-tests for continuous data, and chi-square tests for categorical data (Table 2). We found that variables significantly associated with CKD include, age ≥65 years old, male gender, education level, smoking, alcohol consumption, hypertension, overweight, impaired fasting glucose (IFG), and proteinuria.

Table 2. Comparison between subjects with and without CKD.

Variable		No (*n* = 19,430)		Yes (*n* = 2226)		*p*-Value
		N	%	N	%	
Age	<65	17351	89.3	1004	45.1	<0.001
	≥65	2079	10.7	1222	54.9	
Gender	Female	13398	69.0	1079	48.5	<0.001
	Male	6032	31.0	1147	51.5	
Education level	Uneducated	1132	5.9	391	17.7	<0.001
	Elementary or junior high school	8048	41.7	1131	51.1	
	High school	6009	31.2	408	18.4	
	College or graduate school	4089	21.2	282	12.7	
Smoking	Never	15931	82.0	1733	77.9	<0.001
	Former	1281	6.6	221	9.9	
	Current smoker	2207	11.4	270	12.1	
Chew betel nut	Never	18720	96.5	2151	96.6	0.913
	Former	624	3.2	68	3.1	
	Current	64	0.3	7	0.3	
Hypertension	No	13280	68.5	1166	52.5	<0.001
	Yes	6111	31.5	1053	47.5	
Overweight (BMI ≥ 24)	No	9872	50.9	838	37.7	<0.001
	Yes	9518	49.1	1384	62.3	
Hypercholesteremia (Cholesterol ≥ 200)	No	9230	47.5	1019	45.8	0.121
	Yes	10198	52.5	1207	54.2	
Impaired fasting glucose (IFG) mellitus (AC ≥ 126)	No	18178	93.6	1928	86.6	<0.001
	Yes	1252	6.4	298	13.4	
Protein	-	17543	96.9	1896	88.6	<0.001
	+/-	455	2.5	140	6.5	
	+	60	0.3	50	2.3	
	++	37	0.2	24	1.1	
	+++	12	0.1	31	1.4	

p-value by Chi-square test.

The logistic regression model was used to estimate the odds ratio (OR) of CKD. Variables with significant OR of CKD after univariate analysis were subsequently analyzed by multivariate method (Table 3). We found that distance to open space (every 100 m) has significant odds (1.071) for CKD. Other parameters also have significant odds for CKD include: PM_{coarse} (OR 1.017), age ≥65 (OR 6.812), male (OR 2.741), uneducated (OR 1.714), elementary or junior high school (OR 1.339), overweight (OR 1.308), hypertension (OR 1.184), cholesterol level (OR 1.002), lower red blood count(OR 1.876), higher leukocyte count (OR 1.097), proteinuria +/− (OR 2.156), proteinuria + (OR 5.645), proteinuria ++ (OR 3.701), and proteinuria +++ (OR 15.028).

Forest plot (Table 4) showing subgroup analysis of the risk of CKD in different distance to the open space. The result shows that if residents of the female gender, without hypertension, or without impaired fasting glucose (IFG) living more than 200 m from open spaces, they would have greater odds of CKD than those living less than 200 m from open spaces.

Table 3. Odds ratio for CKD.

Predictor		Total	CKD		Multiple Analysis (Adjusted)			
			N	%	Odds Ratio	95% C.I.		*p*-Value
Distance to open space (100 m)	Mean ± SD	1.17 ± 0.80	1.20 ± 0.83		1.071	1.007	- 1.138	0.029
PM_Coarse (µg/m³)	Mean ± SD	13 ± 3.68	23.29 ± 3.76		1.017	1.003	- 1.031	0.015
Age	<65	18355	1004	5.5	1.000			
	≥65	3301	1222	37.0	6.812	6.100	- 7.607	<0.001
Gender	Female	14477	1079	7.5	1.000			
	Male	7179	1147	16.0	2.741	2.436	- 3.084	<0.001
Education	Uneducated	1523	391	25.7	1.714	1.395	- 2.104	<0.001
	Elementary or junior high school	9179	1131	12.3	1.339	1.147	- 1.562	<0.001
	High school	6417	408	6.4	1.002	0.844	- 1.189	0.983
	College or graduate school	4371	282	6.5	1.000			
Overweight (BMI ≥ 24)	No	10710	838	7.8	1.000			
	Yes	10902	1384	12.7	1.308	1.176	- 1.454	<0.001
Hypertension	No	14446	1166	8.1	1.000			
	Yes	7164	1053	14.7	1.184	1.066	- 1.315	0.002
Protein	-	19439	1896	9.8	1.000			
	+/-	595	140	23.5	2.156	1.717	- 2.707	<0.001
	+	110	50	45.5	5.645	3.593	- 8.866	<0.001
	++	61	24	39.3	3.701	1.954	- 7.010	<0.001
	+++	43	31	72.1	15.028	7.091	- 31.845	<0.001
Cholesterol (mg/dL)	Mean ± SD	204.4 ± 36.5	206.6 ± 38.8		1.002	1.001	- 1.004	0.001
RBC	Mean ± SD	4.0 ± 0.50	4.53 ± 0.57		0.533	0.474	- 0.599	<0.001
WBC	Mean ± SD	6.27 ± 1.60	6.62 ± 1.73		1.097	1.064	- 1.132	<0.001

Table 4. Subgroup analyses of the effect of distance to open space on CKD.

| Subgroup | | Distance to Open Space (m) | | | | | | Odds in >200 m Group Compared to Odds in ≤200 m Group | | | | Interactio |
| | | ≤200 | | | >200 | | | | | | | |
		Total	CKD(eGFR<60) N	%	Total	CKD(eGFR<60) N	%	Forest Plot	Odds	95% C.I.	p-Value [a]	p-Value [b]
	Overall	18531	1871	10.1	3125	355	11.4		1.141	1.012 - 1.287	0.032	
Age	<65	15721	843	5.4	2634	161	6.1		1.149	0.966 - 1.367	0.117	<0.001
	≥65	2810	1028	36.6	491	194	39.5		1.132	0.930 - 1.378	0.215	
Gender	Female	12365	893	7.2	2112	186	8.8		1.241	1.052 - 1.463	0.011	<0.001
	Male	6166	978	15.9	1013	169	16.7		1.062	0.888 - 1.270	0.508	
Overweight(BMI≥24)	No	9165	705	7.7	1545	133	8.6		1.130	0.931 - 1.372	0.215	<0.001
	Yes	9330	1162	12.5	1572	222	14.1		1.156	0.990 - 1.349	0.066	
Hypertension	No	12289	962	7.8	2157	204	9.5		1.230	1.050 - 1.441	0.011	<0.001
	Yes	6201	902	14.5	963	151	15.7		1.092	0.906 - 1.318	0.355	
Impaired fasting	No	17193	1615	9.4	2913	313	10.7		1.161	1.022 - 1.320	0.022	<0.001
	Yes	1338	256	19.1	212	42	19.8		1.044	0.725 - 1.503	0.816	
Smoking	No	15087	1453	9.6	2577	280	10.9		1.144	0.999 - 1.310	0.052	0.008
	Yes	3432	416	12.1	547	75	13.7		1.152	0.884 - 1.501	0.294	

The dashed vertical line indicates the overall odds ratio (1.141), and the solid vertical line indicates no risk (odds ratio = 1.00). p-value a is from test statistics for odds of CKD between distance to open space ≤200 m group and >200 m group; p value b is from test statistics for interaction between distance to open space and subgroup variable.

Table 5 reveals the results of multiple linear regression on eGFR. Variables with significant odds of CKD were selected for this analysis. We found that predictor with the largest negative partial regression coefficient (β) was proteinuria (−4.770). The β value of distance to open space (100 m) and PM$_{Coarse}$ were −0.185 and −0.122, respectively.

Table 5. Multiple linear regression of predictors on eGFR.

Predictor	β	SE	Std β	95% C.I. for β			*p*-Value
(Constant)	128.201	1.032		126.178	to	130.224	<0.001
Distance to open space (100 m)	−0.185	0.083	−0.012	−0.348	to	−0.021	0.027
PM$_{Coarse}$ (µg/m^3)	−0.122	0.018	−0.035	−0.157	to	−0.086	<0.001
Age	−0.599	0.008	−0.452	−0.614	to	−0.584	<0.001
Gender (Male vs. Female)	−4.364	0.164	−0.161	−4.685	to	−4.044	<0.001
BMI (kg/m^2)	−0.082	0.021	−0.022	−0.123	to	−0.041	<0.001
DBP (mm Hg)	−0.025	0.006	−0.024	−0.037	to	−0.013	<0.001
Cholesterol (mg/dL)	−0.007	0.002	−0.019	−0.011	to	−0.003	<0.001
RBC	0.779	0.157	0.030	0.472	to	1.086	<0.001
WBC	−0.257	0.044	−0.032	−0.344	to	−0.170	<0.001
BUN (mg/dL)	−0.807	0.017	−0.269	−0.840	to	−0.773	<0.001
Protein	−4.770	0.330	−0.077	−5.418	to	−4.123	<0.001

β: regression coefficient; Std β: standardized regression coefficient.

4. Discussion

The evidence of the beneficial effects of urban open space on human health is substantial. Prior research revealed that urban open space has many benefits on health. Maas et al. investigated the relationship between physician-assessed morbidity and green space in the living environment of residents [8]. They found lower morbidities caused by anxiety (OR: 0.95), depression (OR: 0.96), coronary heart disease (OR: 0.97), infectious disease of the intestinal canal (OR: 0.97), urinary tract infection (OR: 0.97), musculoskeletal disease (OR: 0.98), and diabetes mellitus (OR: 0.98) among people in residences having green space within 1-km radius. Other benefits of open space on the health of residents in the vicinity include lower blood pressure [10], less obesity [20], decreased mortality of respiratory disease [9], less heat-associated diseases, especially among elderly people with chronic diseases (congestive heart failure, myocardial infarction, chronic obstructive pulmonary disease, and diabetes mellitus) [10] , lower stroke mortality [12], increased longevity of senior citizens [11], less newborns with low birth weight [5,6], and less children with asthma [7].

The mechanisms behind beneficial effects of open space on physical and mental health include enhancing physical activity [2,21] and recovery from stress and attention fatigue [22], respectively. As of social health, open space facilitates of social contact [23], reduces socioeconomic health inequalities [24], while ecologically, is has cooling effects [25], can reduce noise reduction [26] and filter air [27].

Taiwan is a country with a very high population density (649 persons/km^2) and high urbanization. In such a crowded country, open space is very precious, especially in metropolis areas. Besides, the disease burden of CKD in Taiwan is an important public health concern [14,28]. However, to our best knowledge, the relationship between urban open space and human kidney function has not yet been studied. Hence, this study was conducted to explore the association between proximity to urban open space and renal function of residents.

We used logistic regression method to evaluate variables' odds ratio for CKD. Multiple analysis results revealed that 100 m distance to open space had an odds ratio of 1.072 for CKD (Table 3). Results obtained from multiple linear regression on eGFR showed that distance to open space 100 m is associated with lower eGFR (Table 5). These findings are biologically plausible because urban open space facilitates the physical activity of residents [2,29], which in turn is beneficial to renal function [30,31]. Both proximity to green spaces [2] and built environments [29] are revealed to be associated with increased physical activity in the two review studies. Furthermore, previous studies found that better renal function is associated with physical activity. Joseph et al. [30] reviewed the data of the Third National Health and Nutrition Examination Survey (NHANES III) and found a clear association between physical activity and GFR, particularly in adults without metabolic syndrome. Another US study using the NHANES database and estimates subjects' objective physical activity by both accelerometer and questionnaire [31]. They found a positive association of total and light physical activities with renal function. The mechanisms behind the association of physical activity with better renal function include physical activity that leads to better glycemic control in type 2 diabetes mellitus [32] and better BP control. DM and hypertension are the leading causes of CKD. Hyperlipidemia is also a risk factor of CKD and physical activity may also result in better lipid control [33].

The second reason accounting for a better renal function is that urban open space may provide a function of air filtration [34]. McPherson et al. estimated that approximately 9.8 tons of PM_{10} had been removed by trees in the Chicago area per day [35]. On the other hand, air pollution is associated with poorer renal function. A recent longitudinal study explored the association between $PM_{2.5}$ and renal function in older men [36] and found that 1-year $PM_{2.5}$ exposure was associated with a decrease in eGFR of 1.87 mL/min/1.73 m^2. The possible mechanism involved includes inflammation, oxidative stress, blood pressure, and vascular/endothelial function as a result of exposure to air pollutants. With the effect of air filtration of trees, residents living near green spaces may benefit from having better air quality. However, it needs more study to confirm this relationship.

Besides distance to open space, other demographic characteristics and comorbidities of subjects were also examined for their association with renal function. Consistent with previous studies, factors significantly associated with CKD included aged, male gender, uneducated, smoking, hypertension, overweight, impaired fasting glucose (IFG), and proteinuria (Table 2). After multiple analysis of logistic regression of CKD, factors with an odds ratio for CKD included distance to open space, PM_{coarse}, aged, male gender, uneducated, overweight, proteinuria, hypercholesteremia, anemia and leukocytosis (Table 3).

To further explore the effect of distance on CKD, we performed subgroups analysis to compare certain groups of residents who live within 200 m to open space and who live more than 200 m to open space. There are several reasons that we chose 200 m as distance thresholds to access open space. Natural England's Accessible Natural Greenspace Guidance recommends that in order to allow everyone access to natural green space, they should live no more than 300 meters (5 minutes' walk) from home [37]. A Danish survey found that 2000 adults Danes age 18-80 had good access to and use frequently of green space if they lived less than 100 m from it [38]. Pedestrian walking speed is another concern. The walking speed is faster among younger healthy male persons. The 15th percentile walking speed for older pedestrians is 0.67 m per second [39]. Taken together, most aged residents can be access to nearby open space within five minutes if they live no more than 200 m from it.

Subgroups analysis of the risk of CKD found that subjects who were female, without hypertension, and without impaired fasting glucose (IFG) have a significantly higher odds ratio of CKD if they live more than 200 m from open space than those who live less than 200 m (Table 4). In other words, the negative effects of distance to open space on renal function are more prominent among female or relatively healthier residents. One possible reason is that for subjects with comorbidities that were risk factors for CKD, the effects of distance to open space on renal function are relatively much smaller than those who without the comorbidities. Other risk factors of CKD are greater drivers of kidney function loss than the distance to open space. Another possible reason is that the medication for treating the comorbidities may interfere with the association between distance to open space and renal function. Further research is necessary to elucidate the current findings and hypotheses. Anyway, our finding reassures the important role of disease prevention of urban open spaces.

In the current study, gender differences in the relationship between open space and health were also noted in other studies. A study from Dutch explored the relationship between the self-reported health of over 10,000 people and the amount of green space in their living environment. The study found the relationship was stronger for housewives and the elderly [40]. Stafford et al. explored whether associations between neighborhood characteristics and self-rated health are different for men and women in the UK. They found that the influence of the residential environment on women's health was greater than that on men [41]. However, Richardson et al. performed a UK-wide study to explore the gender difference of the association between urban green space and health outcome. They found that cardiovascular disease mortality was associated with urban green space in men, but not in women. The postulated reason is that women have a greater concern of safety issue about green space. Besides, their leisure time exercise was more severely attenuated by having young children than men [42]. In the current study, the gender difference in the relationship between open space and health was noted. The personal safety issue is small in New Taipei City, where the open spaces are relatively small and the population density is high. A possible explanation for the greater influence of residential environments on women's renal function is that housewives spend more time in their neighborhood environment than their husbands do. Taiwan's female employment rate (between 15–65 years old) was only 49.62% in 2009. On the other hand, men may have higher mobility and thus spend more time far away from home. Another possible reason is that gender difference in vulnerability to negative health impacts on renal function.

Information of the general population of New Taipei City >30 years of age in 2009 obtained through the National Health Interview Survey and accessible at the government's web site [43] was analyzed. Compared with the general population of New Taipei City, our subjects were more likely to be overweight (50% vs. 47%) and hypertensive (33% vs. 22%), but less likely to be smokers (11% vs. 20%), consume alcohol (37% vs. 55%), and chew betel nuts (3.5% vs. 8.3%). In terms of education level, our subjects are more likely to be uneducated (7.09% vs. 1.59%), have attended elementary or junior high school (42.71% vs. 35.24%), but less likely to have received college or graduate school education (20.34% vs. 30.49%).

This study we used education level to stand for socioeconomic status and found higher odds of CKD among uneducated subjects (Table 3). This finding is comparable to the result obtained by Mitchell et al. [24] that open space can reduce the negative effect of lower socioeconomic status on health. The incidence rate ratios (IRR) for all-cause mortality in the least and the most greenery area were 1.93 and 1.43, respectively. The effect was also noted in circulatory diseases, with IRR 2.19 in the least green area and 1.54 in the most greenery area. Similar results were also noted by Maas et al. who found a stronger relationship between urban green space and health among lower socioeconomic groups [4]. The physical activity level is lower among people with low socioeconomic status [44]. The reason behind our finding is that if these people live near open space, they have greater access to places for doing exercise. Equity is at the heart of the Sustainable Development Goal (SDG) advocated by the United Nations. Urban open space may promote healthy lives and well-being for all ages (SDG 3), reduce inequalities (SDG 10), and establish sustainable cities and communities (SDG 11).

This study explored the health effects of "open space" rather than "green space", which is more commonly in research conducted in western countries. The reason is that there are very few green spaces in New Taipei City. Most residents are unable to easily access to green space. However, open spaces such as schoolyards are much more available. In order to enhance residents doing exercise, Taiwan enforced "National Sports Act" in 2000. The Article 7 of the Act states: "Sports facilities of all levels of educational institutions should open to the public and provide access to community citizens for sporting activities, under the pretext that it does not affect the teaching and life management of schools [45]." A national survey conducted later by the Sports Administration, Ministry of Education, Taiwan enrolled 15,361 residents revealed that the most common places of exercise are nearby the home (17%) and schools (17%) [46,47]. Many residents of the city do exercise every day in their nearby schools after the classes are over.

One of the strengths of our study is that this may be the first study to explore the relationship between open space and renal function. Second, we used a general survey to explore the health effects of local residents rather than self-rated health perception. Third, this is a large cross-sectional study in an area with high population density performed by the local government. The weakness of our study is that we had not measured subjectively or objectively the real physical activity and types of physical activity of our subjects. However, the relationship between distance to open space and physical activity had been proved by several other studies. Besides, the types of physical activity in our study subjects may be different from that of the western countries. Under the influence of traditional culture, there are many citizens of all ages play Taijiquan in their nearby open spaces such as schoolyards or parks. Some others may also play Chinese boxing, martial arts, or folk dance. The second weakness is that we had not checked the medication taken by our study subjects. Medication may modify the effect of distance to open space on renal health. Third, the serum creatinine level was measured only once. The possibility of laboratory error is a concern. Besides, we had no data about the trend of renal function over time. Further studies are necessary to explore the causal relationship and long-term health effect of urban open spaces on the disease progression of CKD.

5. Conclusions

In conclusion, living more distant from urban open space in New Taipei Metropolis is associated with lower eGFR and higher odds of CKD. The association is stronger in female gender or relatively healthier adults without hypertension or impaired fasting glucose (IFG). Proper urban design is thus essential in Taiwan where prevalence and incidence of CKD are very high. Further researches were necessary to explore whether proximity to open space will also be associated with the renal function of residents in suburban or rural areas.

Author Contributions: conceptualization, C.-C.C.; methodology, C.-C.C.; software, C.-C.C.; validation, C.-C.C.; formal analysis, Y.-R.Y. and S.-Y.C.; investigation, Y.-R.Y. and S.-Y.C.; resources, Y.-R.Y. and S.-Y.C.; data curation, Y.-J.C.; writing—original draft preparation, J.-W.C. and Y.-R.Y.; writing—review and editing, J.-W.C.; visualization, C.-C.C.; supervision, C.-C.C.; project administration, C.-C.C.

Funding: This research received no external funding.

Conflicts of Interest: The authors declare no conflict of interest.

References

1. Siemens, A.G. The Green City Index. A Summary of the Green City Index Research Series. 2015. Available online: http://wikiprogress.org/data/organization/green-city-index (accessed on 15 January 2019).
2. Kaczynski, A.T.; Henderson, K.A. Environmental correlates of physical activity: A review of evidence about parks and recreation. *Leis. Sci.* **2007**, *29*, 315–354. [CrossRef]
3. Pretty, J.; Peacock, J.; Sellens, M.; Griffin, M. The mental and physical health outcomes of green exercise. *Int. J. Environ. Health Res.* **2005**, *15*, 319–337. [CrossRef] [PubMed]
4. Maas, J.; Verheij, R.A.; Groenewegen, P.P.; De Vries, S.; Spreeuwenberg, P. Green space, urbanity, and health: How strong is the relation? *J. Epidemiol. Community Health* **2006**, *60*, 587–592. [CrossRef] [PubMed]
5. Dadvand, P.; de Nazelle, A.; Figueras, F.; Basagaña, X.; Su, J.; Amoly, E.; Jerrett, M.; Vrijheid, M.; Sunyer, J.; Nieuwenhuijsen, M.J. Green space, health inequality and pregnancy. *Environ. Int.* **2012**, *40*, 110–115. [CrossRef] [PubMed]
6. Donovan, G.H.; Michael, Y.L.; Butry, D.T.; Sullivan, A.D.; Chase, J.M. Urban trees and the risk of poor birth outcomes. *Health Place* **2011**, *17*, 390–393. [CrossRef] [PubMed]
7. Lovasi, G.S.; Quinn, J.W.; Neckerman, K.M.; Perzanowski, M.S.; Rundle, A. Children living in areas with more street trees have lower prevalence of asthma. *J. Epidemiol. Community Health* **2008**, *62*, 647–649. [CrossRef] [PubMed]
8. Maas, J.; Verheij, R.A.; de Vries, S.; Spreeuwenberg, P.; Schellevis, F.G.; Groenewegen, P.P. Morbidity is related to a green living environment. *J. Epidemiol. Community Health* **2009**, *63*, 967–973. [CrossRef] [PubMed]
9. Villeneuve, P.J.; Jerrett, M.; Su, J.G.; Burnett, R.T.; Chen, H.; Wheeler, A.J.; Goldberg, M.S. A cohort study relating urban green space with mortality in Ontario, Canada. *Environ. Res.* **2012**, *115*, 51–58. [CrossRef]

10. Zanobetti, A.; O'Neill, M.S.; Gronlund, C.J.; Schwartz, J.D. Summer temperature variability and long-term survival among elderly people with chronic disease. *Proc. Natl. Acad. Sci. USA* **2012**, *109*, 6608–6613. [CrossRef]

11. Takano, T.; Nakamura, K.; Watanabe, M. Urban residential environments and senior citizens' longevity in megacity areas: The importance of walkable green spaces. *J. Epidemiol. Community Health.* **2002**, *56*, 913–918. [CrossRef]

12. Hu, Z.; Liebens, J.; Rao, K.R. Linking stroke mortality with air pollution, income, and greenness in northwest Florida: An ecological geographical study. *Int. J. Health Geogr.* **2008**, *7*, 20–41. [CrossRef] [PubMed]

13. Hsu, C.C.; Hwang, S.J.; Wen, C.P.; Chang, H.Y.; Chen, T.; Shiu, R.S.; Horng, S.S.; Chang, Y.K.; Yang, W.C. High prevalence and low awareness of CKD in Taiwan: A study on the relationship between serum creatinine and awareness from a nationally representative survey. *Am. J. Kidney Dis.* **2006**, *48*, 727–738. [CrossRef] [PubMed]

14. Wen, C.P.; Cheng, T.Y.D.; Tsai, M.K.; Chang, Y.C.; Chan, H.T.; Tsai, S.P.; Chiang, P.H.; Hsu, C.C.; Sung, P.K.; Hsu, Y.H.; et al. All-cause mortality attributable to chronic kidney disease: A prospective cohort study based on 462293 adults in Taiwan. *Lancet* **2008**, *371*, 2173–2182. [CrossRef]

15. Chen, L.I.; Guh, J.Y.; Wu, K.D.; Chen, Y.M.; Kuo, M.C.; Hwang, S.J.; Chien, T.H.; Chen, H.C. Modification of diet in renal disease (MDRD) study and CKD epidemiology collaboration (CKD-EPI) equations for Taiwanese adults. *PLoS ONE* **2014**, *9*, e99645. [CrossRef] [PubMed]

16. United States Environmental Protection Agency. What Is Open Space/Green Space? Available online: https://www3.epa.gov/region1/eco/uep/openspace.html (accessed on 15 January 2019).

17. Eeftens, M.; Beelen, R.; de Hoogh, K.; Bellander, T.; Cesaroni, G.; Cirach, M.; Dimakopoulou, K.; Declercq, C.; Dèdelè, A.; Dons, E.; et al. Development of land use regression models for $PM_{2.5}$, $PM_{2.5}$ absorbance, PM_{10} and PMcoarse in 20 European study areas; results of the ESCAPE project. *Environ. Sci. Technol.* **2012**, *46*, 11195–11205. [CrossRef]

18. Lee, J.H.; Wu, C.F.; Hoek, G.; de Hoogh, K.; Beelen, R.; Brunekreef, B.; Chan, C.C. LUR models for particulate matters in the Taipei metropolis with high densities of roads and strong activities of industry, commerce and construction. *Sci. Total Environ.* **2015**, *514*, 178–184. [CrossRef] [PubMed]

19. Hartig, T.; Evans, G.W.; Jamner, L.D.; Davis, D.S.; Gärling, T. Tracking restoration in natural and urban field settings. *J. Environ. Psychol.* **2003**, *23*, 109–123. [CrossRef]

20. Ellaway, A.; Macintyre, S.; Bonnefoy, X. Graffiti, greenery, and obesity in adults: secondary analysis of European cross sectional survey. *BMJ* **2005**, *331*, 611–612. [CrossRef]

21. Humpel, N.; Owen, N.; Leslie, E. Environmental factors associated with adults' participation in physical activity: A review. *Am. J. Prev. Med.* **2002**, *22*, 188–199. [CrossRef]

22. Sugiyama, T.; Leslie, E.; Giles-Corti, B.; Owen, N. Associations of neighbourhood greenness with physical and mental health: Do walking, social coherence and local social interaction explain the relationships? *J. Epidemiol. Community Health* **2008**, *62*, e9. [CrossRef]

23. Maas, J.; Van Dillen, S.M.; Verheij, R.A.; Groenewegen, P.P. Social contacts as a possible mechanism behind the relation between green space and health. *Health Place* **2009**, *15*, 586–595. [CrossRef] [PubMed]

24. Mitchell, R.; Popham, F. Effect of exposure to natural environment on health inequalities: An observational population study. *Lancet* **2008**, *372*, 1655–1660. [CrossRef]

25. Solecki, W.D.; Rosenzweig, C.; Parshall, L.; Pope, G.; Clark, M.; Cox, J.; Wiencke, M. Mitigation of the heat island effect in urban New Jersey. *Glob. Environ. Chang. B Environ. Hazards* **2005**, *6*, 39–49. [CrossRef]

26. Bolund, P.; Hunhammar, S. Ecosystem services in urban areas. *Ecol. Econ.* **1999**, *29*, 293–301. [CrossRef]

27. Escobedo, F.J.; Nowak, D.J. Spatial heterogeneity and air pollution removal by an urban forest. *Landsc. Urban Plan.* **2009**, *90*, 102–110. [CrossRef]

28. Hwang, S.J.; Lin, M.Y.; Chen, H.C.; Hwang, S.C.; Yang, W.C.; Hsu, C.C.; Chiu, H.H.; Mau, L.W. Increased risk of mortality in the elderly population with late-stage chronic kidney disease: A cohort study in Taiwan. *Nephrol. Dial. Transplant.* **2008**, *23*, 3192–3198. [CrossRef] [PubMed]

29. Sallis, J.F.; Floyd, M.F.; Rodriguez, D.A.; Saelens, B.E. Role of Built Environments in Physical Activity, Obesity, and Cardiovascular Disease. *Circulation* **2012**, *125*, 729–737. [CrossRef] [PubMed]

30. Finkelstein, J.; Joshi, A.; Hise, M.K. Association of physical activity and renal function in subjects with and without metabolic syndrome: A review of the Third National Health and Nutrition Examination Survey (NHANES III). *Am. J. Kidney Dis.* **2006**, *48*, 372–382. [CrossRef] [PubMed]

31. Hawkins, M.S.; Sevick, M.A.; Richardson, C.R.; Fried, L.F.; Arena, V.C.; Kriska, A.M. Association between physical activity and kidney function: National Health and Nutrition Examination Survey. *Med. Sci. Sports Exerc.* **2011**, *43*, 1457–1464. [CrossRef]

32. Boulé, N.G.; Haddad, E.; Kenny, G.P.; Wells, G.A.; Sigal, R.J. Effects of exercise on glycemic control and body mass in type 2 impaired fasting glucose (IFG) mellitus: A meta-analysis of controlled clinical trials. *JAMA* **2001**, *286*, 1218–1227. [CrossRef]

33. Fletcher, B.; Berra, K.; Ades, P.; Braun, L.T.; Burke, L.E.; Durstine, J.L.; Fair, J.M.; Fletcher, G.F.; Goff, D.; Hayman, L.L.; et al. Managing Abnormal Blood Lipids: A Collaborative Approach: Cosponsored by the Councils on Cardiovascular Nursing; Arteriosclerosis, Thrombosis, and Vascular Biology; Basic Cardiovascular Sciences; Cardiovascular Disease in the Young; Clinical Cardiology; Epidemiology and Prevention; Nutrition, Physical Activity, and Metabolism; and Stroke; and the Preventive Cardiovascular Nurses Association. *Circulation* **2005**, *112*, 3184–3209. [CrossRef] [PubMed]

34. Jim, C.; Chen, W.Y. Assessing the ecosystem service of air pollutant removal by urban trees in Guangzhou (China). *J. Environ. Manag.* **2008**, *88*, 665–676. [CrossRef] [PubMed]

35. McPherson, G.E.; Nowak, D.J.; Rowntree, R.A. Chicago's Urban Forest Ecosystem: Results of the Chicago Urban Forest Climate Project. 1994. Available online: https://www.fs.usda.gov/treesearch/pubs/4285 (accessed on 15 January 2019).

36. Mehta, A.J.; Zanobetti, A.; Bind, M.A.C.; Kloog, I.; Koutrakis, P.; Sparrow, D.; Vokonas, P.S.; Schwartz, J.D. Long-Term Exposure to Ambient Fine Particulate Matter and Renal Function in Older Men: The VA Normative Aging Study. *Environ. Health Perspect.* **2016**, *124*, 1353–1360. [CrossRef] [PubMed]

37. England, N. Nature Nearby: Accessible Natural Greenspace Guidance. Natural England: Peterborough 2010. Available online: https://webarchive.nationalarchives.gov.uk/20140605145320/http://publications.naturalengland.org.uk/publication/40004?category=47004 (accessed on 15 January 2019).

38. Nielsen, T.S.; Hansen, K.B. Do green areas affect health? Results from a Danish survey on the use of green areas and health indicators. *Health Place* **2007**, *13*, 839–850. [CrossRef] [PubMed]

39. Chang, C.Y.; Woo, T.H.; Wang, S.F. Analysis of pedestrian walking speeds at crosswalks in Taiwan. *J. East. Asia Soc. Transp. Stud.* **2011**, *9*, 1186–1200. [CrossRef]

40. De Vries, S.; Verheij, R.A.; Groenewegen, P.P.; Spreeuwenberg, P. Natural environments—Healthy environments? An exploratory analysis of the relationship between greenspace and health. *Environ. Plan. A* **2003**, *35*, 1717–1731. [CrossRef]

41. Stafford, M.; Cummins, S.; Macintyre, S.; Ellaway, A.; Marmot, M. Gender differences in the associations between health and neighbourhood environment. *Soc. Sci. Med.* **2005**, *60*, 1681–1692. [CrossRef] [PubMed]

42. Richardson, E.A.; Mitchell, R. Gender differences in relationships between urban green space and health in the United Kingdom. *Soc. Sci. Med.* **2010**, *71*, 568–575. [CrossRef]

43. Health Promotion Administration, Ministry of Health and Welfare. Available online: http://olap.hpa.gov.tw (accessed on 15 January 2019).

44. Popham, F.; Mitchell, R. Relation of employment status to socioeconomic position and physical activity types. *Prev. Med.* **2007**, *45*, 182–188. [CrossRef]

45. Laws & Regulations Database of the Republic of China. National Sports Act. Available online: http://law.moj.gov.tw/Eng/LawClass/LawAll.aspx?PCode=H0120001 (accessed on 15 January 2019).

46. Sports Administration, Ministry of Education, Taiwan. Available online: https://www.sa.gov.tw/wSite/ct?xItem=5457&ctNode=698&mp=11 (accessed on 15 January 2019).

47. Sports Administration, Ministry of Education, Taiwan. Available online: http://www.sa.gov.tw/wSite/public/Data/f1387422688352.pdf (accessed on 15 January 2019).

International Journal of
*Environmental Research
and Public Health*

Article

Neighborhood Built Environment and Socioeconomic Status are Associated with Active Commuting and Sedentary Behavior, but not with Leisure-Time Physical Activity, in University Students

Javier Molina-García [1,2,*], **Cristina Menescardi** [1,2], **Isaac Estevan** [1,2], **Vladimir Martínez-Bello** [1,3] and **Ana Queralt** [2,4]

1   Department of Teaching of Musical, Visual and Corporal Expression, University of Valencia, Avda. dels Tarongers, 4, 46022 Valencia, Spain
2   AFIPS research group, University of Valencia, 46022 Valencia, Spain
3   COS research group, University of Valencia, 46022 Valencia, Spain
4   Department of Nursing, University of Valencia, Jaume Roig, s/n, 46010 Valencia, Spain
*   Correspondence: javier.molina@uv.es; Tel.: +34-961-625-170

Received: 11 July 2019; Accepted: 29 August 2019; Published: 31 August 2019

Abstract: The role of neighborhood characteristics in promoting physical activity and sedentary behaviors (SB) has not been extensively studied in university students. The study purpose was to analyze the associations of neighborhood built environment and neighborhood socioeconomic status (SES) with active commuting, leisure-time physical activity (LTPA), and SB among university students. This is a cross-sectional study of 308 undergraduate students from two urban universities in Valencia, Spain. Participants' residential neighborhoods were classified according to walkability and SES levels. Walkability was defined as an index of three built environment attributes (i.e., residential density, land-use mix, and street connectivity) based on geographical information system data. Active commuting to and from university (ACU), active commuting in the neighborhood, LTPA, and SB were evaluated through a questionnaire. Mixed model regression analyses were performed. There were no significant SES–walkability interactions for any of the outcomes analyzed. However, university students living in more walkable areas reported two more ACU trips per week compared to those living in less walkable neighborhoods ($p < 0.01$). University students living in lower-SES neighborhoods reported more ACU trips per week than those living in higher-SES neighborhoods ($p < 0.05$). Regarding LTPA, there were no significant SES or walkability main effects. Neighborhood SES was negatively related to active commuting in the neighborhood and to time spent in SB (all $p < 0.05$). Participants living in lower-SES neighborhoods reported more active commuting per week and had the highest average minutes spent in SB. This study highlights the relevance of assessing university's residential environment when active transportation and SB are analyzed.

Keywords: exercise; obesity; urban environment; walkability; active transportation; college students

1. Introduction

The beneficial role of physical activity on promoting population health has been extensively demonstrated [1]. Physical inactivity is a global issue that causes noncommunicable diseases such as heart disease, hypertension, diabetes or cancer and reduces life expectancy [2]. In this regard, the transition from high school to university is one of the key life transitions that is characterized by multiple changes in the daily routine and is associated with a significant decrease in physical activity levels [3–5]. Research indicates that regarding international recommendations (i.e., at least 30 min of moderate-to-vigorous physical activity per day in adults [1]), approximately 50% of university students are considered physically inactive [6,7]. Research also suggests that physical activity must be studied through its examination across multiple domains, because this provides deepened understanding of students' physical activity engagement [8].

From an ecological perspective [9], there are different types of factors affecting physical activity behavior in university students. In this regard, individual and psychosocial factors have been the most analyzed in previous research [10–12]. Nevertheless, environmental variables and, more specifically, built environment, have been scarcely analyzed among university students. The built environment refers to human-made surroundings, from small-scale settings (e.g., houses, schools, and offices) to large-scale settings (e.g., neighborhoods, communities, and cities), as well as sidewalks, streets, and green areas [13]. Neighborhoods are one site in which the built environment might be particularly relevant for health, mainly facilitating or hindering physical activity behavior [14,15]. Neighborhood characteristics are one of the most consistent built environmental factors associated with physical activity behavior in the general adult population [9,15]. According to a recent systematic review of the effects of residential relocation on physical activity [16], one of the most consistent activity-promoting neighborhood attributes is walkability. Walkability is an estimation of how much a built environment promotes physical activity [17]. It usually includes components such as residential density, street intersection density, and land use mix [18]. However, the operationalization of the measures of walkability as well as the type or number of built environment factors considered show a large degree of variability [19,20]. For this reason, the International Physical Activity and the Environment Network (IPEN) has developed a set of protocols aimed at maximizing comparability of built environment characteristics and physical activity between different geographical contexts [15]. In the present study, the IPEN walkability index was used [18].

The studies carried out in the general adult population and young people indicate that high levels of walkability of the neighborhood are related with high levels of physical activity [21–23]. Walkable environments have a closer proximity to green areas and other recreational areas (e.g., sport facilities) that can facilitate leisure-time physical activity (LTPA), such as leisure-time walking [24,25]. In the case of the sedentary behaviors (SB), it is hypothesized that low-walkable neighborhoods have few opportunities for physical activity and may lead citizens to spend more time doing recreational sedentary activities (e.g., watching TV) [22]. Nevertheless, in relation to SB, findings in the literature have been inconsistent [22,23,26].

The assessment of the relationship between residential neighborhood walkability and university students' physical activity is virtually non-existent. The limited number of studies has focused on analyzing campus walkability among US university students [27–29]. Recently, Horacek et al. [28] analyzed the characteristics of thirteen US university campuses and demonstrated that more walkable/bikeable environments were associated with more walking for transportation and better weight status. Rybarczyk [29] evaluated the communities surrounding a US university campus and found significant associations between residential density and intersection density with active travel to campus in a sample of faculty, staff, and students. Today, there are no studies that have focused on the analysis of the built environment of the residential neighborhoods of the students from urban universities. Urban universities are more usual in European countries and are characterized by having their schools integrated into the city urban area [30] and not in a closed geographical area, such as university campuses [27,28]. On the other hand, in addition to physical activity behavior, the relationship between neighborhood walkability and SB are unexplored among university students.

Literature has also indicated the existence of socioeconomic differences in built environments [31–33], suggesting that low socioeconomic status (SES) residents may be exposed to less supportive environments for active lifestyles. However, the potential role of high vs. low neighborhood SES in moderating the relationship between urban environment and physical activity or SB has not been evaluated yet in university students. According to Van Dyck et al. [34], understanding if SES variables are effect modifiers is important for several reasons. One of these reasons is related with the necessity of knowing if walkability relates similarly to health behaviors (e.g., physical activity) in high- and low-SES neighborhoods. Moreover, it is important to examine these interactions to reduce health disparities across socioeconomic groups. Literature has also shown that neighborhood SES can have a direct influence on physical activity and SB [23,26]. Nevertheless, the results are inconclusive and seem to differ according to the type of behavior and the population groups analyzed [23,34–36].

The present study examined the associations of neighborhood walkability and neighborhood SES with active commuting, leisure-time physical activity (LTPA), and SB among Spanish university students. In this regard, it was hypothesized that both neighborhood walkability and neighborhood SES influence university students' active commuting, LTPA, and SB.

2. Materials and Methods

2.1. Study Design and Procedure

This study was conducted as part of the IPEN Adolescent study in Spain [23]. Although this study was designed for adolescents, the methodology was adapted to samples of children [31] and university students. A cross-sectional study was designed to recruit participants via convenience sampling in classes. Participants' residential neighborhoods were classified according to walkability and SES levels. The smallest governmental administrative unit (i.e., census blocks) was used to delineate neighborhoods. The city of Valencia consisted of 593 census blocks at the time of the study. Census blocks were objectively evaluated and categorized as high or low walkability/SES using the IPEN walkability index [18]. Based on IPEN recommendations [18,23,37], census blocks were divided into deciles based on their walkability and SES values: The lowest five deciles constituted the "low" category, and the highest five deciles corresponded with the "high" category. Then, based on previous research [23], participants from the census blocks in the central deciles were removed. A 2 × 2 matrix was established by high/low walkability and high/low SES, with the four categories called "quadrants" (Figure 1). The use of binary variables allows comparison with other studies (e.g., [18,23,37]) from diverse types of geographical contexts.

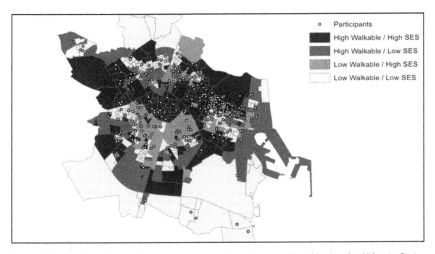

Figure 1. Distribution of the study participants according to the type of neighborhood in Valencia, Spain.

2.2. Participants

Participants were 308 undergraduate students (22.4 years, standard deviation 5.6; 62.0% female) from two urban universities in Valencia (Spain) recruited via convenience sampling in classes. Previously, 11 participants were excluded because of incomplete questionnaire data. Inclusion criteria were: university students living in the city of Valencia during the academic year; and being able to walk without assistance. Data were collected in 2015 during the academic year and were balanced in the 2 × 2 matrix. Once the participants from the census blocks in the central deciles were removed, the final sample was composed of 213 university students. The study protocol was approved by the Human Research Ethics Committee at the corresponding author's university, and informed consent was obtained from the participants before study enrollment.

2.3. *Measures*

2.3.1. Neighborhood Evaluation

The IPEN walkability index score for each census block was calculated using GIS (Geographic Information System) measures of net residential density (ratio of residential units to the land area devoted to residential use), street intersection density (ratio of the number of street intersections to land area of the block-group), and land use mix (diversity of land use types per census block), as described previously (see Frank et al. [18] for more description). The formula for land use mix captures how evenly the square footage of diverse uses is distributed (i.e., residential, office, civic/institutional, recreation, entertainment, food-related, and retail area) and ranges from 0 to 1 [38]. The walkability index was the sum of the z scores of the three built environment measures:

$$\text{Walkability Index} = [(\text{z-score of net residential density}) + (\text{z-score of intersection density}) + (\text{z-score of land use mix})]$$

The educational level of each census block was used as an indicator of SES [23,39]. These data on educational level were obtained through the INE (National Institute of Statistics, Spain) for 2011. Educational level ranged from 0 (illiterate person) to 4 (university training). The average of this variable was calculated in each census block. Then, the z score of the educational level was also calculated. ArcGIS 10.2 software (ESRI, Redlands, CA, USA) was used to generate the GIS variables.

2.3.2. Active Commuting to and from University (ACU)

Modes of transport to and from university were assessed by: "How often do you use each of the following ways to go to and from the university?" [40] Response options were bike, bus, car, train/metro/tram, motorbike, and walking. University students indicated the number of trips per week (to or from university) in each mode of transport. The total number of trips per week they made on foot or by cycling was obtained. This questionnaire has been demonstrated to be acceptably reliable and valid in university students in a previous study [40].

2.3.3. Active Commuting in the Neighborhood, Leisure-Time Physical Activity (LTPA), and Sedentary Behavior (SB)

These physical activity domains were assessed by the Spanish version of the GPAQ survey (Global Physical Activity Questionnaire [41]). The GPAQ was developed and validated by the World Health Organization [41]. The information on the frequency and duration of the active transportation and moderate-and-vigorous-intensity LTPA was collected. In relation to active commuting, university students were asked to report the usual way they travel to and from places (e.g., to work, for shopping and to market). Participants were also asked to report the average sitting time per day as a proxy for SB. The GPAQ questionnaire has been satisfactorily used among Spanish university students in previous research (e.g., [5]).

2.3.4. Covariates

Body mass index (BMI; kg/m^2) was calculated using self-reported weight and height. Access to car and motorbike was also evaluated using two items [12]: "Do you have a car for personal use?"; "Do you have a motorbike for personal use?" Items were rated 1 ("never"), 2 ("sometimes") or 3 ("always"). Type of residence was assessed by "Where do you live during the academic year?" Response options were divided into two categories: family residence (parents' home or own house) and university residence (shared flat with other students or hall of residence). The street-network distance from participants' residence to university school was calculated using GIS procedures. University students were also asked to indicate the number of years living at their current address. Access to public transport was also measured with: "How long does it take you to walk from your home to the nearest public transit? (bus, tram, metro)." Participants responded in minutes. Barriers to ACU were measured using a reliable and valid scale that includes items related to the environment/safety (seven items) and planning/psychosocial factors (seven items) [12]. Example items are: 'There is nowhere to leave a bike safely' and 'I have too much stuff to carry to walk or bike'. This scale uses a response format from 1 ("strongly disagree") to 4 ("strongly agree"). Other covariates were participants' gender and age.

2.4. Statistical Analysis

The analyses were carried out using SPSS v.22.0 (SPSS, Chicago, IL, USA). Descriptive statistics (e.g., means, standard deviations, skewness for continuous measures, frequencies, and percentages) were calculated to analyze the distributions of the measurements.

The main variables of interest, in the models run to address the study's primary purpose, were high- vs. low-neighborhood walkability and high- vs. low-neighborhood SES, as well as the interaction between these two variables. For each outcome variable, the full model (walkability and SES main effects, interactions, and all covariates) was first tested to determine whether there was an SES–walkability interaction effect. To minimize type 2 statistical errors, covariates with $p > 0.15$ were removed using backward-stepwise elimination procedures. Separate mixed effects regression models (using SPSS MIXED) were fit for all the dependent variables (i.e., ACU, active commuting in the neighborhood, LTPA, and SB). Mixed-regression analyses were used so that clustering of participants nested within residential neighborhoods (administrative units), and university schools could be adjusted for as random effects [23]. Sociodemographic measures tested as potential covariates were participant's gender, age, body mass index, access to car/motorbike for personal use, type of residence, number of years living at current address, distance to university, access to public transport, and barriers to ACU.

3. Results

Table 1 indicates the study descriptive statistics for all the participants.

Table 1. Study descriptives for all the sample participants.

Variables	Range	Mean (SD) or %
Sociodemographics		
Body mass index (kg/m^2)	17.6–32.4	22.3 (2.9)
Access to car/motorbike	1–3	1.5 (0.6)
Type of residence (family)	-	56.1
No. of years living at current address	1–33	11.0 (9.4)
Distance to university (km)	0.2–9.9	2.7 (1.8)
Access to public transport (min)	0–20	4.3 (3.6)
Barriers to active commuting to university	1–4	2.4 (0.5)
Outcome variables		
Active commuting to and from university (trips/week)	0–22	8.5 (4.8)
Active commuting in the neighborhood (days/week)	0–7	4.5 (2.5)
Moderate–Vigorous LTPA (min/week)	0–2520	329.8 (387.2)
Moderate LTPA (min/week)	0–1680	154.5 (240.7)
Vigorous LTPA (min/week)	0–900	175.3 (234.2)
Sedentary behavior (min/day)	90–900	400.2 (191.1)

LTPA: leisure-time physical activity.

Figure 2 gives the percentage of trips to and from university by mode of transport per week. A notable percentage of students walked to and from university (47.3% of trips). The percentage of trips by bike was 17.2%, whereas 21.5% was by public transport (train and bus) and 14.0% by private motorized transport (car and motorbike).

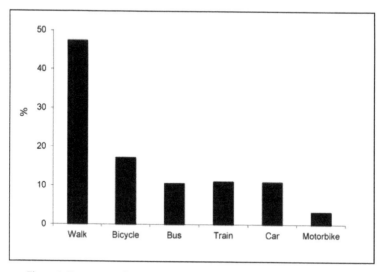

Figure 2. Percentages of trips to and from university by each mode of transport.

Table 2 shows the participants' outcomes by neighborhood-quadrant with covariate-adjusted means. The SES-by-walkability interaction (or SES and walkability main effects, if the interaction was nonsignificant) is also indicated.

Table 2. Participants' active transportation, leisure-time physical activity (LTPA), and sedentary behavior with adjusted means by study-design quadrants and tests for neighborhood socioeconomic status (SES)-by-walkability interaction, or the main effects of SES and walkability without interaction.

Outcome Variables	Adjusted Means (SD)				Tests of significance (p-Value)		
	Low Walkable		High Walkable		SES-by-Walkability Interaction (If p < 0.05)	SES Main Effect (If n.s. Interaction)	Walkability Main Effect (If n.s. Interaction)
	SES		SES				
	Low	High	Low	High			
Active commuting to and from university (trips/week)	8.5 (0.9)	6.6 (0.8)	10.7 (1.0)	8.8 (0.4)	0.506	**0.053**	**0.013**
Active commuting in the neighborhood (days/week)	5.4 (0.5)	4.0 (0.5)	5.7 (0.6)	4.3 (0.2)	0.957	**0.026**	0.521
Moderate–Vigorous LTPA (min/week)	354.2 (94.2)	285.2 (83.0)	415.2 (107.7)	346.2 (55.2)	0.913	0.480	0.442
Moderate LTPA (min/week)	182.5 (56.2)	94.2 (48.2)	260.6 (66.0)	172.2 (24.8)	0.591	0.175	0.139
Vigorous LTPA (min/week)	169.5 (56.7)	192.1 (49.9)	159.5 (64.6)	182.0 (33.0)	0.659	0.702	0.834
Sedentary behavior (min/day)	452.6 (47.8)	353.4 (42.3)	484.5 (52.4)	385.4 (30.8)	0.435	**0.035**	0.415

Note: Bold values indicate statistically significant differences ($p < 0.05$). Models for the main effects contain both walkability and SES factors. Abbreviations: SES, socioeconomic status; LTPA, leisure-time physical activity, n.s.: nonsignificant.

Considering Table 2, there were no significant SES-by-walkability interactions for any of the outcomes analyzed. Nevertheless, ACU showed significant walkability ($p = 0.013$) and SES ($p = 0.053$) main effects. ACU was more frequent overall in higher-walkable and lower-SES areas. University students living in more walkable areas reported more ACU trips per week compared to those living in less walkable neighborhoods (9.7 vs. 7.6 trips, respectively). Likewise, university students living in lower-SES neighborhoods reported about two more trips per week in contrast to those living in higher-SES neighborhoods (9.6 vs. 7.7 trips, respectively).

In relation to active commuting in the neighborhood, there was also one neighborhood SES main effect ($p = 0.026$), with university students living in lower-SES neighborhoods reporting more active days per week than university students living in higher-SES neighborhoods (5.5 vs. 4.1 days, respectively).

Regarding LTPA, there were no significant SES or walkability main effects. However, time spent in SB showed a significant neighborhood SES main effect ($p = 0.035$). The highest average minutes spent in SB (468.6 min/day) was found among university students living in lower-SES areas in contrast to those living in higher-SES areas (average of 369.4 min).

4. Discussion

In a society where transition from high school to university implies an increment of SB [3,5,42] and scarce time of physical activity practice in university students [6,7], it is important to promote healthy lifestyles and contribute to increasing physical activity engagement in this population [8]. The purpose of this cross-sectional study was to examine the associations of neighborhood walkability and neighborhood SES with active commuting, LTPA, and SB among Spanish university students. The results supported that the built environment and/or neighborhood SES are associated with active commuting and SB among Spanish university students.

Transport to university is one of the four life domains contributing to physical activity levels in university students [8]. Systematic review evidence has recently found that ACU can be integrated into overall lifestyle activity to reduce obesity and promote better cardio metabolic health [43]. It should be noted that in the current study, a notable percentage of students actively commutes to and from university on foot (47.3% of trips) and by biking (17.2%). Active commuting on foot or by biking is a good strategy to incorporate physical activity into daily routines among physically inactive populations [44]. In this sense, considering the competing academic and occupational goals in university students [5], ACU might lead to them integrating physical activity engagement in daily routine easier than LTPA in other life domains (e.g., recreational or domestic) and improve healthy levels [45], such as reducing obesity [40,46,47].

Walkability of the neighborhood was a factor that influences ACU. Our main findings indicate that university students who lived in more walkable neighborhoods were more likely to actively travel to university; these students reported two trips more per week compared to those living in less walkable neighborhoods. Similar results were found in children and adolescents [23,31], reinforcing the idea of neighborhood characteristics influence ACU and, consequently, physical activity levels. The results in less walkable neighborhoods could be due to longer, isolated, and unattractive routes discouraging physical activity [44,48]. Perceived walkability is also likely to influence behavior [44,48], but this was not measured in the current study.

In addition, ACU is also associated with the neighborhood SES. In contrast to those students living in higher-SES neighborhoods, counterparts living in lower-SES neighborhoods actively commuted to/from university about twice more per week. Our study also supports previous findings, in which children and adolescents living in lower-SES neighborhoods actively commuted to school frequently [31]. This confirms the assumption that physical activity can be affected by the socioeconomic variables of the neighborhood [49]. Furthermore, there is an association between active commuting in the neighborhood and neighborhood SES. That is, students living in lower-SES areas commuted actively more in their neighborhood than those living in higher-SES neighborhoods (5.5 vs. 4.1 days/week, respectively). This could be due to students from higher-SES areas being able to afford motor vehicles (i.e., cars or motorbikes), and the possibility of access to parking facilities [31]. Considering previous research, it is clear that the use of a motor vehicle is associated with weight gain and increased risk of obesity [47]. As it seems that high-SES students from the current study are more likely to commute passively by driving to university, more active modes of transport should be promoted to favor the adoption of physical activity guidelines.

Regarding SB, an association with neighborhood SES was found. University students living in lower-SES areas spent almost 100 min/day more in SB activities compared to those living in higher-SES areas. It is suggested that among students from low-SES areas, sedentary time is spent on screen time (TV, mobile phone, laptop or computer) [50] because of the lack of sport facilities and organized physical activities promotion in their neighborhood compared to higher-SES neighborhoods [23]. In this sense, it should be noted that SB has also been related to an increase in unhealthy food consumption (e.g., sweets, savory snacks, soda, and soft drinks) and the subsequent risk of obesity [51,52]. With the emerging importance of prolonged sitting time as a chronic disease risk factor, it is important to identify the correlates of SB to develop public health interventions [53].

Regarding LTPA, in the present study, neither neighborhood SES nor walkability were associated with LTPA. These results could be due to university students participating in sports/physical activity classes [23] in different neighborhoods than those in which they live. In this sense, Spanish universities usually offer very varied sports facilities, as well as the possibility of participating in different organized sports activities [10]. Otherwise, the lack of a significant association between walkability and LTPA could be related to the limitations of habitual physical activity measurement through questionnaires [54]. The use of self-reports could be seen as a limitation of the present study because participants usually have a tendency to overreport physical activity and underreport SB [40]. As a more appropriate perspective, it would be desirable that future studies, in university students, use objective measures of physical activity behavior such as motion sensors to determine physical activity level.

Applications for Practice

This study showed a broad group of students (i.e., 64.5%) that travel to/from university on foot, via biking or public transport. However, there is still a significant percentage of university students (14.0%) who do not commute actively. In this line, policy makers could conduct programs for physical activity promotion [55] in universities, especially those aimed at promoting active commuting. In relation to the neighborhood design, street characteristics could be designed to turn streets into a more walkable and bikeable environments. Neighborhoods' infrastructure and aesthetics, in addition to the sense of comfort and safety, promote walkability [55,56]. On the other hand, as it seems that students from high-SES areas passively commute by driving to/from university, a strategy to encourage them to travel actively could be based on reducing the availability and parking access close to university schools or imposing high fees on parking facilities [56,57]. Moreover, as the number of students moving by car increases rapidly with increasing distance, improving accommodation facilities on or near universities (e.g., residences halls or shared flats) could also increase ACU [40]. Similarly, the improvement of public transport connection from students' neighborhoods to university neighborhoods could provide an opportunity to promote ACU [55].

5. Conclusions

This study highlights the relevance of assessing a university's residential environment when active commuting and SB are analyzed. University students living in more walkable areas reported more ACU trips per week compared to those living in less walkable neighborhoods. Moreover, ACU and active commuting in the neighborhood were more frequent in lower-SES areas than in higher-SES neighborhoods. Furthermore, time spent in SB was higher among lower-SES residents.

Author Contributions: J.M.-G. conceived the study, participated in its design and coordination, contributed to data collection, statistical analyses and to the interpretation of results, drafted the manuscript, and approved the final manuscript as submitted. C.M. contributed to the interpretation of the results, drafted sections of the manuscript, and approved the final manuscript as submitted. I.E. participated in the study design, contributed to the interpretation of the results, drafted sections of the manuscript, and approved the final version as submitted. V.M.-B. contributed to the data collection and to the interpretation of the results, reviewed and provided feedback to the manuscript, and approved the final manuscript as submitted. A.Q. participated in the study design, contributed to the data collection and to the interpretation of the results, reviewed and provided feedback to the manuscript, and approved the final manuscript as submitted. All the authors made substantial contributions to the final manuscript.

Funding: This research received no external funding.

Acknowledgments: The authors thank the university students for their participation in the current study.

Conflicts of Interest: The authors declare no conflict of interest. The funders had no role in the design of the study; in the collection, analyses, or interpretation of data; in the writing of the manuscript, or in the decision to publish the results.

References

1. World Health Organization. *Global Action Plan on Physical Activity 2018–2030: More Active People for a Healthier World*; World Health Organization: Geneva, Switzerland, 2018.

2. Lee, I.M.; Shiroma, E.J.; Lobelo, F.; Puska, P.; Blair, S.N.; Katzmarzyk, P.T.; Lancet Physical Activity Series Working Group. Effect of physical inactivity on major non-communicable diseases worldwide: An analysis of burden of disease and life expectancy. *Lancet* **2012**, *380*, 219–229. [CrossRef]

3. Clemente, F.M.; Nikolaidis, P.T.; Martins, F.M.L.; Mendes, R.S. Physical activity patterns in university students: Do they follow the public health guidelines? *PLoS ONE* **2016**, *11*, e0152516. [CrossRef] [PubMed]

4. Deforche, B.; Van Dyck, D.; Deliens, T.; De Bourdeaudhuij, I. Changes in weight, physical activity, sedentary behaviour and dietary intake during the transition to higher education: A prospective study. *Int. J. Behav. Nutr. Phys. Act.* **2015**, *12*, 16. [CrossRef] [PubMed]

5. Molina-García, J.; Queralt, A.; Castillo, I.; Sallis, J.F. Changes in Physical Activity Domains during the Transition out of High School: Psychosocial and Environmental Correlates. *J. Phys. Act. Health* **2015**, *12*, 1414–1420. [CrossRef] [PubMed]

6. Cocca, A.; Liukkonen, J.; Mayorga-Vega, D. Health-related physical activity levels in Spanish youth and young adults. *Percept. Mot. Ski.* **2014**, *118*, 247–260. [CrossRef] [PubMed]

7. Keating, X.D.; Guan, J.; Piñero, J.C.; Bridges, D.M. A meta-analysis of college students' physical activity behaviours. *J. Am. Coll. Health* **2005**, *54*, 116–126. [CrossRef] [PubMed]

8. Murphy, J.J.; MacDonncha, C.; Murphy, M.H.; Murphy, N.; Nevill, A.M.; Woods, C.B. What Psychosocial Factors Determine the Physical Activity Patterns of University Students? *J. Phys. Act. Health* **2019**, *16*, 325–332. [CrossRef]

9. Sallis, J.F.; Owen, N. Ecological models of health behavior. In *Health Behavior: Theory, Research, and Practice*, 5th ed.; Glanz, K., Rimer, B.K., Viswanath, K., Eds.; Jossey-Bass: San Francisco, CA, USA, 2015; pp. 43–64.

10. Molina-García, J.; Castillo, I.; Pablos, C. Determinants of leisure-time physical activity and future intention to practice in Spanish college students. *Span. J. Psychol.* **2009**, *12*, 128–137. [CrossRef]

11. Romaguera, D.; Tauler, P.; Bennasar, M.; Pericas, J.; Moreno, C.; Martinez, S.; Aguilo, A. Determinants and patterns of physical activity practice among Spanish university students. *J. Sports Sci.* **2011**, *29*, 989–997. [CrossRef]

12. Molina-García, J.; Castillo, I.; Sallis, J.F. Psychosocial and environmental correlates of active commuting for university students. *Prev. Med.* **2010**, *51*, 136–138. [CrossRef]

13. Younger, M.; Morrow-Almeida, H.R.; Vindigni, S.M.; Dannenberg, A.L. The built environment, climate change, and health: Opportunities for co-benefits. *Am. J. Prev. Med.* **2008**, *35*, 517–526. [CrossRef] [PubMed]

14. Giles-Corti, B.; Vernez-Moudon, A.; Reis, R.; Turrell, G.; Dannenberg, A.L.; Badland, H.; Foster, S.; Lowe, M.; Sallis, J.F.; Stevenson, M.; et al. City planning and population health: A global challenge. *Lancet* **2016**, *388*, 10–16. [CrossRef]

15. Sallis, J.F.; Cerin, E.; Conway, T.L.; Adams, M.A.; Frank, L.D.; Pratt, M.; Salvo, D.; Schipperijn, J.; Smith, G.; Cain, K.L.; et al. Physical activity in relation to urban environments in 14 cities worldwide: A cross-sectional study. *Lancet* **2016**, *387*, 2207–2217. [CrossRef]

16. Ding, D.; Nguyen, B.; Learnihan, V.; Bauman, A.E.; Davey, R.; Jalaludin, B.; Gebel, K. Moving to an active lifestyle? A systematic review of the effects of residential relocation on walking, physical activity and travel behaviour. *Br. J. Sports Med.* **2018**, *52*, 789–799. [CrossRef] [PubMed]

17. Riley, D.L.; Mark, A.E.; Kristjansson, E.; Sawada, M.C.; Reid, R.D. Neighbourhood walkability and physical activity among family members of people with heart disease who participated in a randomized controlled trial of a behavioural risk reduction intervention. *Health Place* **2013**, *21*, 148–155. [CrossRef] [PubMed]

18. Frank, L.D.; Sallis, J.F.; Saelens, B.E.; Leary, L.; Cain, K.; Conway, T.L.; Hess, P.M. The Development of a Walkability Index: Application to the Neighborhood Quality of Life Study. *Br. J. Sport Med.* **2010**, *44*, 924–933. [CrossRef] [PubMed]

19. Brownson, R.C.; Hoehner, C.M.; Day, K.; Forsyth, A.; Sallis, J.F. Measuring the built environment for physical activity: State of the science. *Am. J. Prev. Med.* **2009**, *36*, S99–S123. [CrossRef]

20. Grasser, G.; Van Dyck, D.; Titze, S.; Stronegger, W.J. A European perspective on GIS-based walkability and active modes of transport. *Eur. J. Public Health* **2016**, *27*, 145–151. [CrossRef]

21. Sallis, J.F.; Saelens, B.E.; Frank, L.D.; Conway, T.L.; Slymen, D.J.; Cain, K.L.; Chapman, J.E.; Kerr, J. Neighborhood Built Environment and Income: Examining Multiple Health Outcomes. *Soc. Sci. Med.* **2009**, *68*, 1285–1293. [CrossRef]

22. Sallis, J.F.; Conway, T.L.; Cain, K.L.; Carlson, J.A.; Frank, L.D.; Kerr, J.; Glanz, K.; Chapman, J.E.; Saelens, B.E. Neighborhood Built Environment and Socioeconomic Status in Relation to Physical Activity, Sedentary Behavior, and Weight Status of Adolescents. *Prev. Med.* **2018**, *110*, 47–54. [CrossRef]

23. Molina-García, J.; Queralt, A.; Adams, M.A.; Conway, T.L.; Sallis, J.F. Neighborhood Built Environment and Socio-Economic Status in Relation to Multiple Health Outcomes in Adolescents. *Prev. Med.* **2017**, *105*, 88–94. [CrossRef] [PubMed]

24. Van Cauwenberg, J.; Nathan, A.; Barnett, A.; Barnett, D.W.; Cerin, E. Relationships between neighbourhood physical environmental attributes and older adults' leisure-time physical activity: A systematic review and meta-analysis. *Sports Med.* **2018**, *48*, 1635–1660. [CrossRef] [PubMed]

25. Queralt, A.; Molina-García, J. Physical Activity and Active Commuting in Relation to Objectively Measured Built-Environment Attributes Among Adolescents. *J. Phys. Act. Health* **2019**, *16*, 371–374. [CrossRef] [PubMed]

26. Van Dyck, D.; Cerin, E.; Conway, T.L.; De Bourdeaudhuij, I.; Owen, N.; Kerr, J.; Cardon, G.; Frank, L.D.; Saelens, B.E.; Sallis, J.F. Associations between perceived neighborhood environmental attributes and adults' sedentary behavior: Findings from the USA, Australia, and Belgium. *Soc. Sci. Med.* **2012**, *74*, 1375–1384. [CrossRef] [PubMed]

27. Roemmich, J.N.; Balantekin, K.N.; Beeler, J.E. Park-like Campus Settings and Physical Activity. *J. Am. Coll. Health* **2015**, *63*, 68–72. [CrossRef] [PubMed]

28. Horacek, T.M.; Dede Yildirim, E.; Kattelmann, K.; Brown, O.; Byrd-Bredbenner, C.; Colby, S.; Greene, G.; Hoerr, S.; Kidd, T.; Koenings, M.M.; et al. Path Analysis of Campus Walkability/Bikeability and College Students' Physical Activity Attitudes, Behaviors, and Body Mass Index. *Am. J. Health Promot.* **2018**, *32*, 578–586. [CrossRef] [PubMed]

29. Rybarczyk, G. Toward a Spatial Understanding of Active Transportation Potential among a University Population. *Int. J. Sustain. Transp.* **2018**, *12*, 1–12. [CrossRef]

30. Chillón, P.; Molina-García, J.; Castillo, I.; Queralt, A. What distance do university students walk and bike daily to class in Spain. *J. Transp. Health* **2016**, *3*, 315–320. [CrossRef]

31. Molina-García, J.; Queralt, A. Neighborhood Built Environment and Socioeconomic Status in Relation to Active Commuting to School in Children. *J. Phys. Act. Health* **2017**, *14*, 761–765. [CrossRef]

32. Steinmetz-Wood, M.; Kestens, Y. Does the Effect of Walkable Built Environments Vary by Neighborhood Socioeconomic Status? *Prev. Med.* **2015**, *81*, 262–267. [CrossRef]

33. Sallis, J.F.; Slymen, D.J.; Conway, T.L.; Frank, L.D.; Saelens, B.E.; Cain, K.; Chapman, J.E. Income Disparities in Perceived Neighborhood Built and Social Environment Attributes. *Health Place* **2011**, *17*, 1274–1283. [CrossRef] [PubMed]

34. Van Dyck, D.; Cardon, G.; Deforche, B.; Sallis, J.F.; Owen, N.; De Bourdeaudhuij, I. Neighborhood SES and walkability are related to physical activity behavior in Belgian adults. *Prev. Med.* **2010**, *50*, S74–S79. [CrossRef] [PubMed]

35. Van Lenthe, F.J.; Brug, J.; Mackenbach, J.P. Neighbourhood inequalities in physical activity: The role of neighbourhood attractiveness, proximity to local facilities and safety in the Netherlands. *Soc. Sci. Med.* **2005**, *60*, 763–775. [CrossRef] [PubMed]

36. McNeill, L.H.; Kreuter, M.W.; Subramanian, S.V. Social environment and physical activity: A review of concepts and evidence. *Soc. Sci. Med.* **2006**, *63*, 1011–1022. [CrossRef] [PubMed]

37. Kerr, J.; Sallis, J.F.; Owen, N.; De Bourdeaudhuij, I.; Cerin, E.; Sugiyama, T.; Reis, R.; Sarmiento, O.; Frömel, K.; Mitás, J.; et al. Advancing Science and Policy through a Coordinated International Study of Physical Activity and Built Environments: IPEN Adult Methods. *J. Phys. Act. Health* **2013**, *10*, 581–601. [CrossRef] [PubMed]

38. Frank, L.D.; Schmid, T.L.; Sallis, J.F.; Chapman, J.; Saelens, B.E. Linking Objectively Measured Physical Activity with Objectively Measured Urban Form: Findings from SMARTRAQ. *Am. J. Prev. Med.* **2005**, *28*, 117–125. [CrossRef] [PubMed]

39. Janssen, E.; Sugiyama, T.; Winkler, E.; de Vries, H.; te Poel, F.; Owen, N. Psychosocial Correlates of Leisure-Time Walking among Australian Adults of Lower and Higher Socio-Economic Status. *Health Edu. Res.* **2010**, *25*, 316–324. [CrossRef]

40. Molina-García, J.; Sallis, J.F.; Castillo, I. Active Commuting and Sociodemographic Factors among University Students in Spain. *J. Phys. Act. Health* **2014**, *11*, 359–363. [CrossRef]

41. Bull, F.C.; Maslin, T.S.; Armstrong, T. Global Physical Activity Questionnaire (GPAQ): Nine Country Reliability and Validity Study. *J. Phys. Act. Health* **2009**, *6*, 790–804. [CrossRef]

42. Kwan, M.Y.; Cairney, J.; Faulkner, G.E.; Pullenayegum, E.E. Physical Activity and Other Health-Risk Behaviors during the Transition into Early Adulthood: A Longitudinal Cohort Study. *Am. J. Prev. Med.* **2012**, *42*, 14–20. [CrossRef]

43. García-Hermoso, A.; Quintero, A.P.; Hernández, E.; Correa-Bautista, J.E.; Izquierdo, M.; Tordecilla-Sanders, A.; Prieto-Benavides, D.; Sandoval-Cuellar, C.; González-Ruíz, K.; Villa-González, E.; et al. Active Commuting to and from University, Obesity and Metabolic Syndrome among Colombian University Students. *BMC Public Health* **2018**, *18*, 523. [CrossRef] [PubMed]

44. Zuñiga-Teran, A.; Orr, B.J.; Gimblett, R.H.; Chalfoun, N.V.; Marsh, S.E.; Guertin, D.P.; Going, S.B. Designing Healthy Communities: Testing the Walkability Model. *Front. Arch. Res.* **2017**, *6*, 63–73. [CrossRef]

45. Dinu, M.; Pagliai, G.; Macchi, C.; Sofi, F. Active Commuting and Multiple Health Outcomes: A Systematic Review and Meta-Analysis. *Sports Med.* **2019**, *49*, 437–452. [CrossRef] [PubMed]

46. Flint, E.; Cummins, S. Active Commuting and Obesity in Mid-Life: Cross-Sectional, Observational Evidence from UK Biobank. *Lancet Biabetes Endocrinol.* **2016**, *4*, 420–435. [CrossRef]

47. Lindström, M. Means of Transportation to Work and Overweight and Obesity: A Population-Based Study in Southern Sweden. *Prev. Med.* **2008**, *46*, 26–28. [CrossRef] [PubMed]

48. Owen, N.; Humpel, N.; Leslie, E.; Bauman, A.; Sallis, J.F. Understanding environmental influences on walking; Review and research agenda. *Am. J. Prev. Med.* **2004**, *27*, 67–76. [CrossRef] [PubMed]

49. Martins, J.; Torres, B.; Cardoso, J.; Costa, A.M.; Honório, S. Influence of Sociological Aspects on the Level of Physical Activity in Physical Education Students. *Hum. Sport Exerc.* **2015**, *10*, 815–826. [CrossRef]

50. Do Carmo, M.; de Castro, B.M.; Barbosa, D.; Meireles, A.L. Are Neighborhood Characteristics Associated with Sedentary Behavior in Adolescents? A Systematic Review. *Int. J. Environ. Health Res.* **2019**. [CrossRef]

51. Santaliestra-Pasías, A.M.; Mouratidou, T.; Verbestel, V.; Huybrechts, I.; Gottrand, F.; Le Donne, C.; Cuenca-García, M.; Díaz, L.E.; Kafatos, A.; Manios, Y.; et al. Food Consumption and Screen-Based Sedentary Behaviors in European Adolescents: The HELENA Study. *Arch. Pediatr. Adolesc. Med.* **2012**, *166*, 1010–1020. [CrossRef]

52. Kozo, J.; Sallis, J.F.; Conway, T.L.; Kerr, J.; Cain, K.; Saelens, B.E.; Frank, L.D.; Owen, N. Sedentary Behaviors of Adults in Relation to Neighborhood Walkability and Income. *Health Psychol.* **2012**, *31*, 704–713. [CrossRef]

53. Owen, N.; Sugiyama, T.; Eakin, E.E.; Gardiner, P.A.; Tremblay, M.S.; Sallis, J.F. Adults' Sedentary Behavior: Determinants and Interventions. *Am. J. Prev. Med.* **2011**, *41*, 189–196. [CrossRef] [PubMed]

54. Shepard, R.J. Limits to the Measurement of Habitual Physical Activity by Questionnaires. *Br. J. Sport Med.* **2003**, *37*, 197–206. [CrossRef] [PubMed]

55. Sallis, J.F.; Cervero, R.B.; Ascher, W.; Henderson, K.A.; Kraft, M.K.; Kerr, J. An Ecological Approach to Creating More Physically Active Communities. *Annu. Rev. Public Health* **2006**, *27*, 297–322. [CrossRef] [PubMed]

56. Hynes, M.; Seoighthe, E. Heading in the Right Direction? Investigating Walkability in Galway City, Ireland. *Urban Sci.* **2018**, *2*, 31. [CrossRef]
57. Edwards, P.; Tsouros, A.D. *Promoting Physical Activity and Active Living in Urban Environments: The Role of Local Governments*; WHO Regional Office Europe: Copenhagen, Denmark, 2006.

International Journal of
Environmental Research and Public Health

Article

Density of Green Spaces and Cardiovascular Risk Factors in the City of Madrid: The Heart Healthy Hoods Study

Elena Plans [1,2,†], **Pedro Gullón** [1,3,*,†], **Alba Cebrecos** [1], **Mario Fontán** [1,4], **Julia Díez** [1], **Mark Nieuwenhuijsen** [5,6,7] **and Manuel Franco** [1,8]

[1] Public Health and Epidemiology Research Group, School of Medicine, Universidad de Alcala, 28871 Madrid, Spain; elena.plans@gmail.com (E.P.); alba.cebrecos@uah.es (A.C.); fontan.vela@gmail.com (M.F.); Julia.diez@uah.es (J.D.); mfranco@uah.es (M.F.)
[2] Servicio de Medicina Preventiva y Gestión de Calidad, Hospital General Universitario Gregorio Marañón, 28007 Madrid, Spain
[3] Urban Health Collaborative, Drexel Dornsife School of Public Health, Philadelphia, PA 19104, USA
[4] Servicio de Medicina Preventiva, Hospital Universitario Infanta Leonor, 28031 Madrid, Spain
[5] ISGlobal, Center for Research in Environmental Epidemiology (CREAL), 08036 Barcelona, Spain; mark.nieuwenhuijsen@isglobal.org
[6] Department of Biomedicine, Universitat Pompeu Fabra (UPF), 08002 Barcelona, Spain
[7] Centro de Investigación Biomédica en Red de Epidemiología y Salud Pública (CIBERESP), 28029 Madrid, Spain
[8] Department of Epidemiology, Johns Hopkins Bloomberg School of Public Health, Baltimore, MD 21205, USA
* Correspondence: pedro.gullon@edu.uah.es; Tel.: +34-675-139-946
† These authors contributed equally to this work.

Received: 29 October 2019; Accepted: 3 December 2019; Published: 5 December 2019

Abstract: The aim of this study is to evaluate the relationship between the density of green spaces at different buffer sizes (300, 500, 1000 and 1500 m) and cardiovascular risk factors (obesity, hypertension, high cholesterol, and diabetes) as well as to study if the relationship is different for males and females. We conducted cross-sectional analyses using the baseline measures of the Heart Healthy Hoods study ($N = 1625$). We obtained data on the outcomes from clinical diagnoses, as well as anthropometric and blood sample measures. Exposure data on green spaces density at different buffer sizes were derived from the land cover distribution map of Madrid. Results showed an association between the density of green spaces within 300 and 500 m buffers with high cholesterol and diabetes, and an association between the density of green spaces within 1500 m buffer with hypertension. However, all of these associations were significant only in women. Study results, along with other evidence, may help policy-makers creating healthier environments that could reduce cardiovascular disease burden and reduce gender health inequities. Further research should investigate the specific mechanisms behind the differences by gender and buffer size of the relationship between green spaces and cardiovascular risk factors.

Keywords: green spaces; cardiovascular risk factors; gender; obesity; hypercholesterolemia; hypertension; diabetes

---

1. Introduction

Cardiovascular diseases (CVD) are the leading cause of death worldwide [1,2]. The global number of deaths from CVD has increased globally during the last decade. In fact, in 2016, CVD were responsible for 17.9 million deaths [2], representing one of the major challenges for public health [3]. One of the reasons for this is the increasing prevalence of individual modifiable cardiovascular risk factors, such as obesity, high blood pressure, high cholesterol levels, or diabetes, as well as environmental factors (air pollution, noise, etc.) [4]. In fact, it is estimated that, in Spain, 21.6% of adults are obese [5], 42.6% have hypertension [6], 44.9% high cholesterol [7], and 13,8% diabetes mellitus [8]. Moreover, there is a gender gap in CVD and CVD risk factors; females tend to have a worse risk factor profile compared to males and are more susceptible to risk-factor comorbidity [9].

In the last years, there has been an increasing interest in potential population prevention approaches that could reduce cardiovascular risk factors and, in turn, prevent CVD [10]. Cities present unique opportunities to apply these population prevention approaches, as by definition they are dense, and characterized by substantial man-made components and frequent social interactions [11]. For instance, there is mounting evidence that the availability of parks and other green spaces has benefits for the health and health-related behaviors of urban residents [12,13]. There are different theories that suggest that green spaces affect health through different pathways, such as reducing harm (mitigating exposures to heat, noise, and air pollution), relieving mental and physiologic stress, and promoting healthy activities such as physical activity [14,15].

Previous evidence linked residential green spaces with cardiovascular health and cardiovascular risk factors. There is evidence that a high amount of green spaces is associated with a decrease in cardiovascular mortality [16], a lower hazard of CVD [17], a lower cardiovascular risk [18], and some cardiovascular risk factors, such as obesity [19] and high blood pressure [20]. However, there is no consistent pattern of associations with cardiovascular risk factors, especially in adults, as some studies found green spaces to be associated with a decrease in CVD risk factors while others found no associations [12,13]. Moreover, some studies have suggested that there is a potential effect modification by gender that could change the relationship between green spaces and cardiovascular risk [13,19]. Thus, this study aims to study the relationship between urban green space density and cardiovascular risk factors (obesity, hypertension, high cholesterol, and diabetes) and to study if the relationship is different for males and females.

2. Materials and Methods

2.1. Study Design and Setting

This study is an observational cross-sectional study aiming to study the relationship between the density of green spaces around the residential location and cardiovascular risk factors in the city of Madrid, Spain. In 2016, Madrid had a population of 3.2 M residents and was divided into 21 districts that housed 128 neighborhoods. Within each neighborhood, there are small geographical administrative units of ~1500 people each, called census sections (*N* = 2415) [21].

2.2. Study Population

This study uses the baseline measures of the Heart Healthy Hoods (HHH) cohort. The HHH cohort includes 1720 residents of Madrid that (1) were 40–75 years old in 2017, (2) lived in Madrid (and in the same home address for, at least, one year), (3) were born in Spain or the Andean countries (Ecuador, Peru, Colombia or Bolivia, as that they represent 72.6% of all the South-Americans living in Madrid, and South-Americans are the largest group of migrant residents in Madrid). We excluded potential participants that (a) had previous cardiovascular disease, (b) were institutionalized population, (c) expected to travel outside Madrid more than 3 months per year, (d) were immobilized at home or with terminal or serious conditions that could alter their blood sample values or regular activities, (e) could not answer the telephone questionnaires, (f) planned to move outside Madrid in the following three years.

The sample selection process was carried out in a two-stage process. We first selected 30 primary health care (PHC) centers capturing spatial and sociodemographic variability in the city of Madrid, and then randomized potential participants that met the selection criteria from the PHC physicians' patient list. Spain's National Health System is publicly funded, providing universal health care coverage free of charge at the point of use. Every resident has a primary health care physician and a primary health care center assigned to public insurance. The data used for this study was collected through a clinical visit of the participants with their primary health care physician. From the original sample of 2265 potential participants, 1720 attended the clinical visit. In this clinical visit, participants answered a questionnaire with sociodemographic variables, family history of cardiovascular disease and cardiovascular risk factors, quality of life measures, as well as took anthropometric (blood pressure, body mass index) and blood sample tests (fasting blood glucose and low-density-lipoproteins—LDL). The previous diagnosis of cardiovascular risk factors was obtained through their electronic health records. For this study, we excluded participants that did not have complete information on cardiovascular risk factors, anthropometric measures, or blood tests ($N = 95$, 5.5%), leaving a final sample of 1625 participants for the statistical analyses. The 1720 participants that attended the clinical visit had a similar distribution of age, sex, and migration status compared to the original sample of 2265. The HHH study was conducted according to the guidelines laid down in the Declaration of Helsinki and received IRB approval from the Ethics Research Committee of the Madrid Health Care System on 12 May 2015.

2.3. Exposure: Density of Green Spaces

We obtained all green spaces land cover categories from the General Urban Plan of the City of Madrid for the year 2016, and we extracted those with a size greater than 0.5 hectares, as a minimum size for doing physical activity [15]. The General Urban Plan of the City of Madrid contains information on official land use categories of all blocks, plots, and spaces in the city of Madrid. We took all green spaces categories available as a land use category, including urban parks as well as other neighborhood green spaces. A detailed classification of all categories used for our definition of green spaces can be found in Supplementary File S1. The land cover distributions and Madrid's Urban Plan are publicly available at Madrid's Open Data (https://datos.madrid.es/).

From the General Urban Plan data, we calculated the percentage of green land cover from the population-weighted centroid of the participants' residence census section. Madrid's census sections have an average size of 0.2 km^2, so they are widely used for neighborhood characterization [21]. We used a population-weighted centroid instead of a geometric centroid to avoid locate residents in a non-residential area (likely to be green space) and reduce the risk of misclassification using census measures for the exposure. Thus, we used ArcGIS 10.1 software (v.10.1, ESRI, Redlands, CA, USA) to calculate the percentage of green land cover using different street network buffers (300 m, 500 m, 1000 m and 1500 m) from the population-weighted centroid of each census-section.

2.4. Outcome: Cardiovascular Risk Factors

Four individual modifiable cardiovascular risk factors were our main outcome variables: obesity, hypertension, high cholesterol, and diabetes. We classified as obese those participants that had in their electronic health records a diagnosis of obesity, and those participants that had a BMI greater or equal to 30 kg/m^2, based on the anthropometric measurements [22]. For the latter, we computed the average BMI from the three different measurements that the doctor took during the same clinical visit. For hypertension, we classified as having hypertension those participants previously diagnosed with hypertension (by the electronic health records), those participants in treatment for hypertension and those participants with a mean systolic blood pressure ≥ 140 mmHg or a mean diastolic blood pressure ≥ 90 mmHg after three blood pressure measures during the same clinical visit, following European Society of Cardiology's recommendations [23]. Hypercholesterolemia was defined as previously diagnosed hypercholesterolemia, cholesterol treatment or LDL greater than 160 mg/dL [24]. We classified as having diabetes those participants with clinical records of diabetes, diabetes treatment or fasting plasma glucose ≥ 126 mg/dL [24].

2.5. Covariates

Age, sex, and migration status were self-reported by participants and registered in the clinical visit. To account for the effects of area characteristics, we also adjusted our analyses for the area-level (census section) socioeconomic status (SES) where participants resided in. We used an SES index that includes seven indicators: (1) low education; (2) high education; (3) part-time employment; (4) temporary employment; (5) manual occupational class; (6) average housing prices (per m^2); (7) unemployment rate [25]. We included population density (number of residents/km^2) at the census section using annual population data from Padron (a continuous and universal census collected for administrative purposes) [26].

2.6. Data Analysis

We conducted an exploratory and descriptive analysis of the exposure, outcomes, and covariates. For continuous variables, we calculated medians and interquartile range; for categorical variables, frequency tables.

To study the relationship between the availability of green spaces within 300, 500, 1000 and 1500 m buffers with cardiovascular risk factors, we estimated odds ratios (ORs) of each cardiovascular risk factor with a set of logistic mixed-effects (also known as multilevel) regression models. Thus, each model included a cardiovascular risk factor as the dependent variable, and the availability of green spaces (at 300, 500, 1000, or 1500 m) as the main explanatory variable (divided into quartiles, where *Q1* represents the greatest availability of green spaces and it is used as the reference value). Separate models were calculated for each density (300, 500, 1000 and 1500 m). All models were adjusted by sex, age, migration status, census-section SES, and population density, and included a random intercept for the census section. Thus, the general formula for all these models is

$$\text{Logit (odds for risk factor}_{ij}) = \beta_0 + \beta_1{}^*\text{density(Q2)}_j + \beta_2{}^*\text{density(Q3)}_j + \beta_3{}^*\text{density(Q4)}_j + \beta_4{}^*\text{age}_{ij} + \beta_5{}^*\text{sex}_{ij} + \beta_6{}^*\text{migration}_{ij} + \beta_7{}^*\text{SES}_j + \beta_8{}^*\text{pop density}_j + u_j + e_{ij}$$

where *i* indexes every participant and *j* every census section. β_1, β_2, and β_3 are the coefficients for *Q2*, *Q3*, and *Q4* of green spaces density, respectively. β_4–β_8 are the coefficients for the covariates. u_j and e_{ij} represent the census-section and the individual residual, respectively, both following a normal distribution (0, σ^2).

We then ran the same models stratified by females and males to obtain specific estimates by gender. In addition to this, to formally obtain an overall statistical *p*-value for effect modification, we ran new models introducing an interaction term between sex and density (in this case, introduced as linear). This way we were able to get a *p*-value for the interaction between sex and density (as linear) instead of an interaction term between each quartile and sex. These models were as follows:

$$\text{Logit (odds for risk factor}_{ij}) = \beta_0 + \beta_1{}^*\text{density(as linear)}_j + \beta_2{}^*\text{age}_{ij} + \beta_3{}^*\text{sex}_{ij} + \beta_4{}^*\text{migration}_{ij} + \beta_5{}^*\text{SES}_j + \beta_7{}^*\text{pop density}_j + \beta_8{}^*\text{density(as linear)}_j{}^*\text{sex}_{ij} + u_j + e_{ij}$$

Statistical significance was set at $p = 0.05$; thus, all 95% CI that did not include 1 were considered statistically significant. All analyses and plots were conducted with R V3.5.1. Multilevel models were calculated using the *glmer* function in the *lme4* package.

3. Results

Table 1 shows the characteristics of the study sample, stratified by quartiles of the percentage of green spaces within a 500 m buffer of the census section. The median age was 56 (IQR = 15), 56.06% of the sample were female, and 19.38% of the participants were born outside Spain. The prevalence of obesity, hypertension, high cholesterol and diabetes was 28.43%, 25.35%, 30.69%, and 8.43%, respectively. Population density and socioeconomic status were higher where participants had a lower density of green spaces.

Table 1. Characteristics of the Heart Healthy Hoods (HHH) cohort study sample, stratified by quartiles of % of green space density within 500 m buffer of participants' census section centroid (*N* = 1625).

Individual Characteristics	Total		Q1 (High)		Q2		Q3		Q4 (Low)	
						Quartiles of Green Space Density (within 500 m)				
Age [1] (years)	56	15	56	16	56	14.75	56	14.75	56	15
Sex [2] (female)	911	56.06%	234	57.64%	230	56.65%	225	55.42%	222	54.55%
Migration status [2]	315	19.38%	80	19.70%	84	20.69%	81	19.95%	70	17.20%
Obesity [2]	462	28.43%	120	29.56%	123	30.30%	110	27.09%	109	26.78%
Hypertension [2]	412	25.35%	105	25.86%	93	22.91%	110	27.09%	104	25.55%
High cholesterol [2]	502	30.89%	116	28.57%	119	29.31%	121	29.80%	146	35.87%
Diabetes [2]	137	8.43%	28	6.90%	44	10.84%	32	7.88%	33	8.11%
Population density [1] (pop/km^2)	30,784	23,067	27,333	28,610	28,391	20,360	29,604	21,766	36,840	20,643
Socioeconomic status index [1]	−0.37	1.24	−0.40	0.81	−0.44	0.90	−0.42	0.94	0.17	1.93

[1] Median and IQR. [2] N and %.

In the regression models adjusted by all co-variates, we did not find any association between the density of green spaces and obesity and hypertension (Table 2). For high cholesterol, we found an increased odds of having high cholesterol with decreases in the density of green spaces, especially within 300, 500 and 1000 m buffers (only in *Q4*); for instance, living in the quartile with the lowest density of green spaces at 300, 500, and 1000 m (*Q4*) was associated with an increased odds of high cholesterol of 46% (95% CI: 5% to 103%), 47% (95% CI: 5% to 106%), and 55% (95% CI: 10% to 118%), respectively. There was a relationship between the density of green spaces within a 500 m buffer and diabetes (only in *Q2*); the odds of having diabetes increased by 67%, in *Q2* (95% CI: 1% to 176%); however, it was not significant for *Q3* and *Q4*.

Table 2. Association between the density of green space around the participants' residence (300, 500, 1000 and 1500 m buffers) and cardiovascular risk factors in Madrid (*N* = 1625). Mixed-effects logistic regression models adjusted by age, sex, migration status, population density, and area-level socioeconomic status.

Green Spaces	300 m		500 m		1000 m		1500 m	
	OR [1]	CI 95% [2]	OR	CI 95%	OR	CI 95%	OR	CI 95%
				Obesity				
Q1 (ref)	1 (ref)		1 (ref)		1 (ref)		1 (ref)	
Q2	1.05	(0.76–1.43)	1.05	(0.77–1.44)	0.95	(0.69–1.29)	1.14	(0.84–1.56)
Q3	1.08	(0.79–1.48)	0.89	(0.65–1.22)	0.91	(0.67–1.25)	1.20	(0.88–1.65)
Q4 (Low)	1.00	(0.72–1.38)	1.09	(0.78–1.52)	0.95	(0.67–1.34)	1.05	(0.73–1.52)
				Hypertension				
Q1 (ref)	1 (ref)		1 (ref)		1 (ref)		1 (ref)	
Q2	0.98	(0.71–1.37)	0.84	(0.60–1.18)	0.89	(0.64–1.25)	1.32	(0.93–1.85)
Q3	1.01	(0.72–1.40)	1.06	(0.76–1.47)	1.05	(0.76–1.46)	1.38	(0.98–1.95)
Q4 (Low)	0.92	(0.65–1.30)	1.03	(0.72–1.46)	1.06	(0.74–1.53)	1.20	(0.81–1.79)
				High Cholesterol				
Q1 (ref)	1 (ref)		1 (ref)		1 (ref)		1 (ref)	
Q2	1.28	(0.93–1.77)	1.05	(0.76–1.44)	1.11	(0.80–1.53)	0.90	(0.65–1.24)
Q3	1.32	(0.95–1.83)	1.06	(0.77–1.46)	0.97	(0.70–1.33)	1.04	(0.75–1.43)
Q4 (Low)	1.46	(1.05–2.03)	1.47	(1.05–2.06)	1.55	(1.10–2.18)	1.20	(0.83–1.71)
				Diabetes				
Q1 (ref)	1 (ref)		1 (ref)		1 (ref)		1 (ref)	
Q2	1.61	(0.98–2.64)	1.67	(1.01–2.76)	1.01	(0.62–1.67)	1.15	(0.70–1.87)
Q3	1.15	(0.68–1.95)	1.15	(0.68–1.96)	1.05	(0.64–1.72)	0.97	(0.58–1.61)
Q4 (Low)	1.09	(0.63–1.90)	1.44	(0.82–2.52)	0.99	(0.56–1.75)	1.00	(0.55–1.83)

[1] OR, Odds ratio. [2] CI, Confidence interval.

In the gender-stratified models, we found that female participants showed higher OR than males in the relationship between green spaces and cardiovascular risk factors (Figure 1 and Supplementary Table S2). For obesity, there were no significant associations neither in males or females and the interaction was non-significant; however, within the 1500 m buffer, there was a non-significant increase in odds of having obesity with decreasing density, but only in female participants. In the case of hypertension, we found a relationship between the density of green spaces within a 1500 m buffer and an increased odds of hypertension, but only in females. For instance, females living in Q3 of green space density within a 1500 m buffer had an increased odds of 73% (95% CI: 10% to 173%) for hypertension. Despite this, the interaction term between density and sex was non-significant for all densities in hypertension. For high cholesterol, the associations observed in the non-stratified models were only still present in the models with females. Thus, there were increased odds for high cholesterol for females living in the areas with a low density of green spaces within 500 and 1000 m buffers. For diabetes, we found an association between 300 m and 500 m buffers of green space density and diabetes only in females (interaction term between sex and density for 300 m $p = 0.06$; for 500 m $p = 0.27$); for instance, females living in Q2, Q3, and Q4 of lower green space density (300 m) had an OR of 2.88 (95% CI: 1.17 to 7.10), 2.59 (95% CI: 1.02 to 6.52), and 2.32 (95% CI: 0.86; to 6.18), respectively.

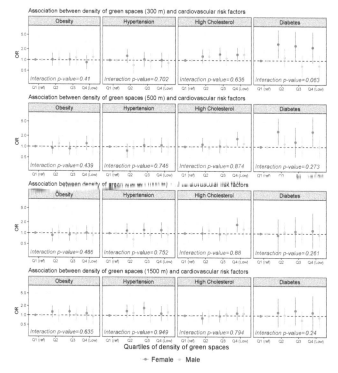

Figure 1. Association between the density of green spaces around participants' residences (300, 500, 1000 and 1500 m buffers) and cardiovascular risk factors in Madrid ($N = 1625$). Mixed-effects logistic regression models were stratified by females (red) and males (blue) and adjusted by age, migration status, population density, and area-level socioeconomic status. Rows represent the different density of green spaces around the home. From top to bottom: 300 m, 500 m, 1000 m and 1500 m. Columns represent each of the cardiovascular risk factors, from left to right: obesity, hypertension, high cholesterol, and diabetes. The interaction p-values represent the interaction between sex and the density of green spaces (as linear instead of categorical).

4. Discussion

4.1. Key Findings

In this study, we found a moderate association between density of green spaces around participant's location (within 300, 500, 1000 and 1500 m buffers) and hypertension, high cholesterol, and diabetes, but not for obesity; particularly, females living in areas of lower green space density had greater odds for specific cardiovascular risk factors (hypertension, high cholesterol, and diabetes) compared to those that live in the highest density areas (*Q1*). These results are relevant because they deepen the knowledge on the relationship between green spaces and cardiovascular health in the specific case of the city of Madrid, and they open new questions regarding the gender dimension in the studies of green spaces and cardiovascular health.

4.2. Comparison with Previous Studies and Mechanisms

Despite the lack of evidence of our results for obesity, other studies found an inverse relationship between the increased availability of green spaces and obesity [27]. We hypothesize two main reasons that could explain why we did not find an association between the density of green spaces and obesity. First, we did not take into account any measure of the quality of green spaces. If we hypothesize that green spaces might prevent obesity through physical activity, these spaces should be designed for that. In fact, there are studies that suggest that certain characteristics of green spaces such as size, sports facilities, quality of paths, and a safe environment might be relevant for physical activity within green spaces [28,29]; for instance, Kaczynski et al. [28] observed that the quality of park trails and the number of facilities and amenities in the park were associated with park-based physical activity. Second, green spaces are usually located in areas with less population and retail density due to lack of space, and these areas might discourage walking and physical activity as they are less walkable [30]. Despite adjusting by population density as a proxy of walkability, we did not test effect modification by population density/walkability; meaning that we did not assess if the relationship between green spaces and obesity is stronger or weaker in areas with high walkability.

Females living in areas with a lower density of green spaces (at 1500 m) had higher odds for hypertension after adjusting by individual and neighborhood characteristics. Previous studies support the idea that greater availability of green spaces around home reduces blood pressure in adults [31,32], especially by harm reduction (e.g., exposure to noise or air pollution) [33], psychological and physiological stress alleviation, increased social cohesion, or physical activity [15]. Similarly, we found a relationship between green spaces and hypercholesterolemia, consistent with other previous studies [27,31,34], that suggested that green spaces could reduce cholesterol levels via physical activity, harm reduction or psychosocial pathways. However, we did not test the mediating pathways through which green spaces might reduce blood pressure or cholesterol levels. Lastly, we also found an association of green spaces density (300 m and 500 m) and diabetes in females, consistent with other studies [35,36]. However, mechanisms behind the association between green spaces and diabetes are not so clear; for instance, Dalton et al. [35] found that physical activity did not mediate the relationship between green spaces and diabetes, and Bodicoat et al. [36] did not find that physical activity and other risk factors explained this association.

4.3. Effect of Gender and Buffer Size

Overall, we only found a relationship between green spaces and cardiovascular risk factors (hypertension, high cholesterol, and diabetes) in female participants. A previous systematic review suggested that the association of green spaces and most mortality outcomes was greater in women and that more research was needed on the different effects of green spaces in males and females [12]. Gender differences in the relationship between green spaces and health have been found in other studies. In fact, previous studies have found stronger effects of green spaces on health for women [19,37], while others not [38]. Indeed, one study found an interaction between age, gender, and the association between green spaces with health; whilst the benefit of greater local green space for men was apparent primarily in early to mid-adulthood, the benefit for women occurred later in life, in their mid−40 s and older [39] (similar to our sample). One possible explanation to the gender differences is that males and females have different social use and perception of green spaces; for instance, males are more likely than females to use green spaces for physical activity [40] and females may not use green spaces if they perceive them as unsafe [41]; in fact, a systematic review with systematic social observation found that, when using green spaces, females seem to be more sedentary than male [42]. However, this would explain only the physical activity pathway, not alternative pathways such as reduced exposure to air pollution and noise. Moreover, our results go against this hypothesis as they go in the opposite direction (green spaces might have more benefit for females). An alternative hypothesis might be that women have stronger benefits of green spaces as they spent more time in the surrounding neighborhood as they may feel socially responsible for housekeeper activities; in fact, a previous study found that the relationship between greenspace and health was stronger for housewives [43]. Future studies should clarify the pathways through which gender interacts in the association between green spaces and health. Unexpected, most of the interaction terms were non-significant. However, this could be because the interaction term between density (as linear) and sex assumed a linear relationship between exposure and outcome (which is not always the case in this study). Despite this fact, we observed that the sub-group analysis that most OR (especially in diabetes) were higher for women. We should also consider that the use of stratified models might have caused a loss in statistical power to detect more statistically significant associations by gender.

Another important key result of our study is the different buffer effects depending on the risk factor. We found that the relationship of green spaces density and hypertension was only present in larger buffers (1000 and 1500 m); while the relationship of green spaces and high cholesterol or diabetes was stronger for smaller buffers (300 and 500 m). Some studies suggested that larger buffers have stronger associations with health outcomes [37] as well as they might better represent distances that people are willing to do for visiting parks and green spaces [43]; however, most of the studies did not find evidence of different effects by buffer size, and suggests that buffer size selection might depend on the context of cities (density, spatial configuration, etc.) [12]. It should be taken into account that we used the population-weighted centroid as the start of our buffers instead of the participants' exact residence, and smaller buffers (300 m) might be subjected to misclassification.

4.4. Strengths and Limitations

This study presents several strengths. Firstly, we were able to test different buffer sizes, providing more insights into how different sizes might be more important for different pathways between green spaces and health. Secondly, we used the street network instead of Euclidean buffers to calculate distances and more accurately adjust the true density of green spaces. Thirdly, despite the common use of satellite-derived land cover distributions and surrounding greenness, such as the Normalized Difference Vegetation Index (NDVI) [14], land use data from the Urban Plan of the City of Madrid is an official tool used by urban planners and policymakers in Madrid, so it might be relevant for policy change. Lastly, we were able to combine two different measures for defining participants with cardiovascular risk factors: practitioners' previous diagnoses (by electronic health records) and anthropometric measures (blood pressure and BMI) obtained in a clinical visit, which could reduce information bias compared to self-reported measures or the use of electronic health records alone.

We are aware that this study has several limitations. This is a cross-sectional study, which does not allow us to claim causality of our results. Besides, we have not taken into account the amount of time that each person has been visiting green spaces, so in future studies, just like Paquet et al. [44], we suggest comparing the association between the group of residents with different time exposure to green spaces, even though visiting green spaces is not the only pathway that could explain this association (as said above, other hypothetical pathways might be, for instance, the reduction of air pollution, heat, and noise). We did not include measures of quality of green spaces (as the quality of trails, safety, etc.), which might influence the use of these spaces. Our exposure measures (density of green spaces) were calculated from the census-section population-weighted centroid instead of the exact residence location, which could lead to a misclassification in the exposure; however, census sections are small spatial units (average size: 0.2 km^2), thus we don't expect a significant misclassification of residence location. Moreover, the use of a population-weighted centroid prevents us to locate the centroid in a non-residential area (which might be a green area). Our stratified models by male and female might have caused a loss in statistical power to detect more statistically significant associations by gender. Lastly, we were not able to test for the specific pathways through which green spaces are connected with cardiovascular risk factors; future studies should study the pathways between green spaces and cardiovascular risk factors with a gender perspective.

5. Conclusions

We found a moderate protective relationship between green space density and several cardiovascular risk factors in female participants; hypercholesterolemia, hypertension, and diabetes, but not for obesity. We found different effects for females and males and for different buffer distances: there was a stronger association with hypertension when using larger buffers, while small buffers showed stronger associations with hypercholesterolemia and diabetes. Future studies should further study the mechanisms of this association, as well as the different effects by buffer size and gender so policy-makers can design urban policies to prevent cardiovascular risk taking into account the differences in the effects by gender.

Supplementary Materials: The following are available online at http://www.mdpi.com/1660-4601/16/24/4918/s1, File S1: Types of green spaces according to General Urban Plan of the city of Madrid, Table S2: Association between density of green space around the participants' residence (300, 500, 1000 and 1500 m buffers) and cardiovascular risk factors in Madrid.

Author Contributions: P.G., E.P. and M.F. (Manuel Franco) conceptualized and designed the study; A.C., P.G. and J.D. prepared the data; E.P. and P.G. wrote the first draft; A.C. performed the spatial analyses; P.G. and E.P. performed statistical analyses and interpreted the data; M.N., M.F. (Manuel Franco), J.D. and M.F. (Mario Fontán) critically revised the paper for intellectual content; P.G. and M.F. (Manuel Franco) performed project supervision and administration, and managed funding acquisition.

Funding: This project was funded by the Instituto de Salud Carlos III, Subdirección General de Evaluación y Fomento de la Investigación, Government of Spain (PI18/00782) and by the European Research Council under the European Union's Seventh Framework Programme (FP7/2007–2013/ERC Starting Grant Heart Healthy Hoods Agreement no. 623 336893). P.G. was supported by the 2018 Alfonso Martín Escudero Research Grant.

Acknowledgments: We would like to thank Heart Healthy Hood's cohort participants as well as the Primary Health Care physicians and telephone interviewers for their time and their assistance in data collection. A previous version of this work, as part of a master's thesis, is available at https://repisalud.isciii.es/bitstream/20.500.12105/8487/1/RelacionDistanciaDensidadParques_2019.pdf.

Conflicts of Interest: The authors declare no conflict of interest.

References

1. Joseph, P.; Leong, D.; McKee, M.; Anand, S.S.; Schwalm, J.-D.; Teo, K.; Mente, A.; Yusuf, S. Reducing the Global Burden of Cardiovascular Disease, Part 1. *Circ. Res.* **2017**, *121*, 677–694. [CrossRef] [PubMed]

2. Townsend, N.; Wilson, L.; Bhatnagar, P.; Wickramasinghe, K.; Rayner, M.; Nichols, M. Cardiovascular disease in Europe: Epidemiological update 2016. *Eur. Heart J.* **2016**, *37*, 3232–3245. [CrossRef] [PubMed]

3. WHO. *Global Status Report on Noncommunicable Diseases 2014*; WHO: Geneva, Switzerland, 2014.

4. Chow, C.K.; Lock, K.; Teo, K.; Subramanian, S.; McKee, M.; Yusuf, S. Environmental and societal influences acting on cardiovascular risk factors and disease at a population level: A review. *Int. J. Epidemiol.* **2009**, *38*, 1580–1594. [CrossRef] [PubMed]

5. Aranceta-Bartrina, J.; Pérez-Rodrigo, C.; Alberdi-Aresti, G.; Ramos-Carrera, N.; Lázaro-Masedo, S. Prevalence of General Obesity and Abdominal Obesity in the Spanish Adult Population (Aged 25–64 Years) 2014–2015: The ENPE Study. *Rev. Española Cardiol.* **2016**, *69*, 579–587. [CrossRef]

6. Menéndez, E.; Delgado, E.; Fernández-Vega, F.; Prieto, M.A.; Bordiú, E.; Calle, A.; Carmena, R.; Castaño, L.; Catalá, M.; Franch, J.; et al. Prevalencia, diagnóstico, tratamiento y control de la hipertensión arterial en España. Resultados del estudio Di@bet.es. *Rev. Esp. Cardiol.* **2016**, *69*, 572–578. [CrossRef] [PubMed]

7. Guallar-Castillón, P.; Gil-Montero, M.; León-Muñoz, L.M.; Graciani, A.; Bayán-Bravo, A.; Taboada, J.M.; Banegas, J.R.; Rodríguez-Artalejo, F. Magnitude and management of hypercholesterolemia in the adult population of Spain, 2008–2010: The ENRICA study. *Rev. Esp. Cardiol.* **2012**, *65*, 551–558. [CrossRef]

8. Soriguer, F.; Goday, A.; Bosch-Comas, A.; Bordiú, E.; Calle-Pascual, A.; Carmena, R.; Casamitjana, R.; Castaño, L.; Castell, C.; Catalá, M.; et al. Prevalence of diabetes mellitus and impaired glucose regulation in Spain: The Di@bet.es Study. *Diabetologia* **2012**, *55*, 88–93. [CrossRef]

9. De Smedt, D.; De Bacquer, D.; De Sutter, J.; Dallongeville, J.; Gevaert, S.; De Backer, G.; Bruthans, J.; Kotseva, K.; Reiner, Ž.; Tokgözoğlu, L.; et al. The gender gap in risk factor control: Effects of age and education on the control of cardiovascular risk factors in male and female coronary patients. the EUROASPIRE IV study by the European Society of Cardiology. *Int. J. Cardiol.* **2016**, *209*, 284–290. [CrossRef]

10. ROSE, G. Sick Individuals and Sick Populations. *Int. J. Epidemiol.* **1985**, *14*, 32–38. [CrossRef]

11. Franco, M.; Bilal, U.; Diez-Roux, A.V. Preventing non-communicable diseases through structural changes in urban environments. *J. Epidemiol. Community Health* **2015**, *69*, 509–511. [CrossRef]

12. Fong, K.C.; Hart, J.E.; James, P. A Review of Epidemiologic Studies on Greenness and Health: Updated Literature Through 2017. *Curr. Environ. Health Rep.* **2018**, *39*, 11–28. [CrossRef] [PubMed]

13. James, P.; Banay, R.F.; Hart, J.E.; Laden, F. A Review of the Health Benefits of Greenness. *Curr. Epidemiol. Rep.* **2015**, *2*, 218. [CrossRef]

14. Nieuwenhuijsen, M.J.; Khreis, H.; Triguero-Mas, M.; Gascon, M.; Dadvand, P. Fifty shades of green. *Epidemiology* **2017**, *28*, 63–71. [CrossRef]

15. Markevych, I.; Schoierer, J.; Hartig, T.; Chudnovsky, A.; Hystad, P.; Dzhambov, A.M.; de Vries, S.; Triguero-Mas, M.; Brauer, M.; Nieuwenhuijsen, M.J.; et al. Exploring pathways linking greenspace to health: Theoretical and methodological guidance. *Environ. Res.* **2017**, *158*, 301–317. [CrossRef]

16. Gascon, M.; Triguero-Mas, M.; Martínez, D.; Dadvand, P.; Rojas-Rueda, D.; Plasència, A.; Nieuwenhuijsen, M.J. Residential green spaces and mortality: A systematic review. *Environ. Int.* **2016**, *86*, 60–67. [CrossRef]

17. Tamosiunas, A.; Grazuleviciene, R.; Luksiene, D.; Dedele, A.; Reklaitiene, R.; Baceviciene, M.; Vencloviene, J.; Bernotiene, G.; Radisauskas, R.; Malinauskiene, V.; et al. Accessibility and use of urban green spaces, and cardiovascular health: Findings from a Kaunas cohort study. *Environ. Health A Glob. Access Sci. Source* **2014**, *13*, 1–11. [CrossRef]

18. Yeager, R.; Riggs, D.W.; DeJarnett, N.; Tollerud, D.J.; Wilson, J.; Conklin, D.J.; O'Toole, T.E.; McCracken, J.; Lorkiewicz, P.; Xie, Z.; et al. Association between residential greenness and cardiovascular disease risk. *J. Am. Heart Assoc.* **2018**, *7*, e009117. [CrossRef]

19. Astell-Burt, T.; Feng, X.; Kolt, G.S. Greener neighborhoods, slimmer people evidence from 246 920 Australians. *Int. J. Obes.* **2014**, *38*, 156–159. [CrossRef]

20. Bijnens, E.M.; Nawrot, T.S.; Loos, R.J.; Gielen, M.; Vlietinck, R.; Derom, C.; Zeegers, M.P. Blood pressure in young adulthood and residential greenness in the early-life environment of twins. *Environ. Health* **2017**, *16*, 53. [CrossRef]

21. Cebrecos, A.; Escobar, F.; Borrell, L.N.; Díez, J.; Gullón, P.; Sureda, X.; Klein, O.; Franco, M. A multicomponent method assessing healthy cardiovascular urban environments: The Heart Healthy Hoods Index. *Health Place* **2019**, *55*, 111–119. [CrossRef]

22. World Health Organization. Obesity and Overweight Fact Sheet. Available online: https://www.who.int/en/news-room/fact-sheets/detail/obesity-and-overweight (accessed on 20 October 2019).

23. Williams, B.; Mancia, G.; Spiering, W.; Agabiti Rosei, E.; Azizi, M.; Burnier, M.; Clement, D.L.; Coca, A.; de Simone, G.; Dominiczak, A.; et al. 2018 ESC/ESH Guidelines for the management of arterial hypertension. *Eur. Heart J.* **2018**, *39*, 3021–3104. [CrossRef] [PubMed]

24. Grant, P.J.; Chairperson, E.; Germany, S.D.A.; France, N.D.; Uk, C.D.; Germany, H.H.; France, M.M.; Germany, N.M.; Poland, M.T.; France, P.V.; et al. ESC Guidelines on diabetes, pre-diabetes, and cardiovascular diseases developed in collaboration with the EASD the European Society of Cardiology (ESC) and developed in collaboration. *Eur. Heart J.* **2013**, *34*, 3035–3087.

25. Gullón, P.; Bilal, U.; Cebrecos, A.; Badland, H.M.; Galán, I.; Franco, M. Intersection of neighborhood dynamics and socioeconomic status in small-area walkability: The Heart Healthy Hoods project. *Int. J. Health Geogr.* **2017**, *16*, 21. [CrossRef] [PubMed]

26. Instituto Nacional de Estadística Estadística del Padrón Continuo. Available online: www.ine.es (accessed on 29 August 2019).

27. Mena, C.; Fuentes, E.; Ormazábal, Y.; Palomo-Vélez, G.; Palomo, I. Role of access to parks and markets with anthropometric measurements, biological markers, and a healthy lifestyle. *Int. J. Environ. Health Res.* **2015**, *25*, 373–383. [CrossRef] [PubMed]

28. Kaczynski, A.T.; Potwarka, L.R.; Saelens, P.B.E. Association of park size, distance, and features with physical activity in neighborhood parks. *Am. J. Public Health* **2008**, *98*, 1451–1456. [CrossRef]

29. Bancroft, C.; Joshi, S.; Rundle, A.; Hutson, M.; Chong, C.; Weiss, C.C.; Genkinger, J.; Neckerman, K.; Lovasi, G. Association of proximity and density of parks and objectively measured physical activity in the United States: A systematic review. *Soc. Sci. Med.* **2015**, *138*, 22–30. [CrossRef]

30. Hosking, J.; Woodward, A.; MacMillan, A.; Smith, M.; Witten, K.; Baas, P.; Mackie, H.; Field, A. Systematic literature review of built environment effects on physical activity and active transport—An update and new findings on health equity. *Int. J. Behav. Nutr. Phys. Act.* **2017**, *14*, 1–27.

31. Brown, S.C.; Lombard, J.; Wang, K.; Byrne, M.M.; Toro, M.; Plater-Zyberk, E.; Feaster, D.J.; Kardys, J.; Nardi, M.I.; Perez-Gomez, G.; et al. Neighborhood greenness and chronic health conditions in medicare beneficiaries. *Am. J. Prev. Med.* **2016**, *51*, 78–89. [CrossRef]

32. Yang, B.Y.; Markevych, I.; Bloom, M.S.; Heinrich, J.; Guo, Y.; Morawska, L.; Dharmage, S.C.; Knibbs, L.D.; Jalaludin, B.; Jalava, P.; et al. Community greenness, blood pressure, and hypertension in urban dwellers: The 33 Communities Chinese Health Study. *Environ. Int.* **2019**, *126*, 727–734. [CrossRef]

33. Hirabayashi, S.; Nowak, D.J. Comprehensive national database of tree effects on air quality and human health in the United States. *Environ. Pollut.* **2016**, *215*, 48–57. [CrossRef]

34. Kim, H.-J.; Min, J.-Y.; Kim, H.-J.; Min, K.-B. Parks and Green Areas Are Associated with Decreased Risk for Hyperlipidemia. *Int. J. Environ. Res. Public Health* **2016**, *13*, 1205. [CrossRef] [PubMed]

35. Dalton, A.M.; Jones, A.P.; Sharp, S.J.; Cooper, A.J.M.; Griffin, S.; Wareham, N.J. Residential neighbourhood greenspace is associated with reduced risk of incident diabetes in older people: A prospective cohort study. *BMC Public Health* **2016**, *16*, 1–10. [CrossRef] [PubMed]

36. Bodicoat, D.H.; O'Donovan, G.; Dalton, A.M.; Gray, L.J.; Yates, T.; Edwardson, C.; Hill, S.; Webb, D.R.; Khunti, K.; Davies, M.J.; et al. The association between neighbourhood greenspace and type 2 diabetes in a large cross-sectional study. *BMJ Open* **2014**, *4*, 1–8. [CrossRef] [PubMed]

37. Bos, E.H.; van der Meulen, L.; Wichers, M.; Jeronimus, B.F. A primrose path? Moderating effects of age and gender in the association between green space and mental health. *Int. J. Environ. Res. Public Health* **2016**, *13*, 492. [CrossRef] [PubMed]

38. Richardson, E.A.; Mitchell, R. Gender differences in relationships between urban green space and health in the United Kingdom. *Soc. Sci. Med.* **2010**, *71*, 568–575. [CrossRef]

39. Astell-Burt, T.; Mitchell, R.; Hartig, T. The association between green space and mental health varies across the lifecourse. a longitudinal study. *J. Epidemiol. Community Health* **2014**, *68*, 578–583. [CrossRef]

40. Cohen, D.A.; McKenzie, T.L.; Sehgal, A.; Williamson, S.; Golinelli, D.; Lurie, N. Contribution of public parks to physical activity. *Am. J. Public Health* **2007**, *97*, 509–514. [CrossRef]

41. Ho, C.H.; Sasidharan, V.; Elmendorf, W.; Willits, F.K.; Graefe, A.; Godbey, G. Gender and ethnic variations in urban park preferences, visitation, and perceived benefits. *J. Leis. Res.* **2005**, *37*, 281–306. [CrossRef]

42. Evenson, K.R.; Jones, S.A.; Holliday, K.M.; Cohen, D.A.; McKenzie, T.L. Park characteristics, use, and physical activity: A review of studies using SOPARC (System for Observing Play and Recreation in Communities). *Prev. Med. (Balt.)* **2016**, *86*, 153–166. [CrossRef]

43. De Vries, S.; Verheij, R.A.; Groenewegen, P.P.; Spreeuwenberg, P. Natural environments—Healthy environments? An exploratory analysis of the relationship between greenspace and health. *Environ. Plan. A* **2003**, *35*, 1717–1731. [CrossRef]

44. Paquet, C.; Orschulok, T.P.; Coffee, N.T.; Howard, N.J.; Hugo, G.; Taylor, A.W.; Adams, R.J.; Daniel, M. Are accessibility and characteristics of public open spaces associated with a better cardiometabolic health? *Landsc. Urban Plan.* **2013**, *118*, 70–78. [CrossRef]

International Journal of
Environmental Research and Public Health

Article

Benefits of A Three-Day Bamboo Forest Therapy Session on the Psychophysiology and Immune System Responses of Male College Students

Bingyang Lyu, Chengcheng Zeng, Shouhong Xie, Di Li, Wei Lin, Nian Li, Mingyan Jiang, Shiliang Liu and Qibing Chen *

College of Landscape Architecture, Sichuan Agricultural University, Chengdu 611130, China;
beyonglv@163.com (B.L.); zcclandscape@163.com (C.Z.); xieshouhong798@163.com (S.X.);
frank0707@126.com (D.L.); landscape1990@163.com (W.L.); nli@sicau.edu.cn (N.L.); jmy@sicau.edu.cn (M.J.);
liushiliang9@163.com (S.L.)
* Correspondence: cqb@sicau.edu.cn

Received: 24 October 2019; Accepted: 5 December 2019; Published: 8 December 2019

Abstract: Forest therapy is a fast-growing treatment approach, as it has the potential to alleviate stressful life events and to improve psychological well-being and physical health. Bamboo forests are widespread in southwestern China. Nevertheless, a knowledge gap on the specific health benefits of bamboo forest (BF) therapy still exists. To explore the psycho-physiologic responses of participants to the effects of BF therapy, 60 male adults aged between 19 and 24, with similar healthy conditions, were selected to participate in this study. A one-group pretest–posttest design was used for the BF sites and the city site (CS) to compare the difference in the psycho-physiologic responses of participants before and after the test. Participants at the BF sites participated in a three-day bamboo forest therapy session, and those at the CS participated in a three-day urban program. Blood pressure, heart rate, and peripheral oxygen saturation were measured as the physical signs, and the profile of mood state (POMS) questionnaire was completed by the participants for the psychological evaluation. Blood was sampled, and natural killer (NK) activity, the number of NK cells, and the levels of corticosterone, granulysin, perforin, and granzyme A/B in peripheral blood lymphocytes (PBLs) were measured. All the measurements mentioned above were performed at 08:00 on the first and fourth days within the test. Results indicated that the three-day BF therapy was capable of enhancing positive mood states and also reducing negative mood states in the male participants. The blood pressure and heart rates of the male participants decreased, while the peripheral oxygen saturation increased after the three-day BF therapy session. Furthermore, BF therapy significantly increased NK activity and the number of NK cells and perforin-, granulysin-, and granzyme A/B-expressing cells and significantly decreased the corticosterone level in PBLs in the male participants. The three-day BF therapy session improved the psychological and physiological well-being and enhanced the immune functions of the male college students.

Keywords: bamboo forest therapy; psychological responses; physiological responses; immune system

---

1. Introduction

As urbanization progresses around the globe, many advantages of developed infrastructures and artificialized urban environments might be closely related to negative health outcomes in modern people [1]. However, given workplace limitations and the appeal of urban life, an increasing number of people prefer to live in large cities rather than rural areas, especially college graduate students. This trend is projected to continue and intensify [2]. As human society becomes increasingly urbanized, various physiological and psychological diseases are caused by stress, thus affecting well-being and health [3]. Research has shown that high blood pressure (BP) costs the U.S. approximately $48.6 billion per year and affects 1 in 3 Americans [4]. In China, the phenomenon of poor health in urban populations is remarkable because the proportion of people with poor health is as high as 76% [5]. College students have several health risk factors, including irregular sleep patterns, personal relationship changes, over-drinking, and academic pressures, and they experience a large amount of stress, anxiety, and depression [6]. Previous studies have shown that approximately 50% of college students experience significant levels of stress, anxiety, or depression, or a combination of these conditions [7]. Evidence has shown that people suffer pressure from the urban environment psychologically and physiologically.

Air pollution, noise pollution, water pollution, work pressure, and other stresses related to urban environments are increasingly compelling people to seek forms of stress relief and healthy lifestyles [8,9]. Because of the negative environmental impacts in urban areas, research on the benefits of immersion in the natural environment is important. The 16th century Swiss-German physician Paracelsus declared the following: "The art of healing comes from nature, not from the physician" [10]. In most people, the relationship between survival and the natural environment is inseparable. Studies have indicated that natural environments have the potential to improve the relationship between stressful life events and psychological well-being and physical health [11–14].

An immersive forest experience known as 'forest therapy' has recently received widespread attention as a novel form of psychological therapy for reducing stress and providing a feeling of relaxation. Forest therapy is a fast-growing treatment approach [15], and researchers have sought to improve the description and evaluation of the relationship between forests and human health [16]. Recent field studies on forest therapy have provided interesting scientific data supporting the hypothesis that physiological indices, such as BP, pulse rate, heart rate variability [3,17], and salivary cortisol concentration [18], were decreased after forest therapy. Moreover, compared with a city setting, a forest therapy program led to a significant increase in parasympathetic nerve activity [19] and lower sympathetic nerve activity [17]. Additionally, some research has shown that compared with the urban environment, forest therapy was capable of enhancing positive mood states and reducing negative mood states as specific psychological responses [20–23]. In addition, forest therapy trips resulted in an increase in natural killer (NK) cell activity, which was mediated by increases in the number of NK cells and the levels of intracellular granulysin, perforin, and granzymes A/B in peripheral blood lymphocytes (PBLs) [24–26].

Bamboo is an important forest type in many countries, especially in East and Southeast Asia and in African countries. It is a versatile and important component of the ecology, culture, and economy of these countries [27,28]. Bamboo is a well-known and the most preferred plant in the Chinese landscape design due to its unique beautiful foliage and fast-growing characteristics. However, to our knowledge, the benefits of bamboo forest (BF) therapy on both psycho-physiological and immune system responses have not been investigated experimentally. We hypothesized that BF therapy would also provide benefits similar to those of forest therapy on psychophysiology and the immune system.

In the current research, we investigated the effectiveness of a BF therapy program on the psychophysiology and immune system of a large sample of male college students through field experiments with a one-group pretest–posttest design. The aim of the present study was to investigate the benefits of a three-day BF therapy session on the psychophysiology and immune system of male college students. Further, the mechanism of interactions between the nervous, endocrine and immune systems in participants after bamboo forest therapy was discussed in the present study.

2. Materials and Methods

2.1. Subjects and Experimental Sites

All experimental sites used in this study were located in Sichuan Province in Southwest China. The city site (CS) in Chengdu was located in the center of downtown. In Chengdu, the subjects could view urban buildings, cars, people and other urban elements. For the bamboo forest (BF) sites, a site located near the city of Ya'an was selected. Ya'an is famous for pandas. The dominant forest species of the selected site (and Sichuan Province) is *Neosinocalamus affinis*, a large species of cluster bamboo. The Yibin site was located in Yibin City, which is well known for the Shunan Bamboo Sea, an AAAA-level scenic area as denoted by the Chinese National Tourism Administration. The Shunan Bamboo Sea comprises more than 12,000 ha of large *Phyllostachys heterocycla*. The Dujiangyan site was a bamboo park named 'zhuhai dongtian' covered with *Phyllostachys praecox 'Prevernalis'* in Dujiangyan City. The average height of bamboo forest is 24.5 m and the average density is 600 tufts per hectare. Figure 1 shows the locations of the four research study sites in Sichuan Province in our study, and Figure 2 shows photographs of the four sites.

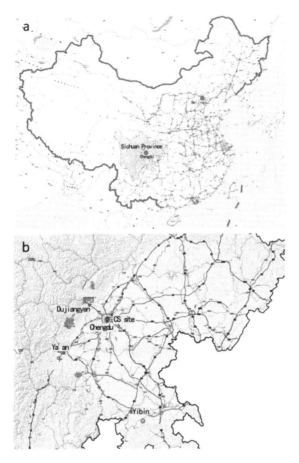

Figure 1. Sketch of experimental sites in the current study. (**a**) Sichuan Province in China and (**b**) the four sites in Sichuan Province. The red points mark the downtown areas and the green points mark the location of each site.

Figure 2. Photographs of the studied sites. (**a**) The city site (CS) site was located at a crossroad in a typical urban environment with cars, buildings, markets, hotels and companies. (**b–d**) The bamboo forests sites.

In this study, 60 male college students from Sichuan Agricultural University participated in three-day field experiments. None of the participants reported any physiological or psychiatric disorders in their personal histories. Subjects who smoked or were alcoholic were excluded from this study. Before the experiment, the goal and experimental procedures of the study were explained to the participants, and their informed consent was obtained. This study was reviewed and approved by the Ethics Committee of Sichuan Agricultural University. To control the background environmental conditions, identical single rooms and similar meals were provided to each subject for the duration of the study period. The subjects were randomly divided into four groups, and each group included 15 males. In addition, basic characteristics of the participants, such as the age, height and weight of each subject, were measured. To avoid physiological differences, the systolic blood pressure (SBP), diastolic blood pressure (DBP), heart rate (HR) and blood oxygen saturation levels of each participant were measured. After collecting the basic data of the participants, analysis of variance was used for the data comparison between the CS and BF experimental sites. The results showed no significant differences between the CS and BF experimental sites in the subjects' age, height, or weight. The results are shown in Table 1.

Table 1. Basic information of the sampling subjects at the CS and bamboo forest (BF) sites included in this study. Body mass index (BMI) = weight (kg)/[height (m)]^2. All data are presented as the mean ± SEs. CS, city site; BF, bamboo forest sites.

Parameter	CS	BF
Sample No. (count)	15	45
Age (years)	21.6 ± 0.34	21.8 ± 0.25
Weight (kg)	65.5 ± 1.23	64.1 ± 0.82
Height (cm)	175.2 ± 0.50	174.6 ± 0.49
BMI (kg m^{-2})	21.3 ± 0.45	20.9 ± 0.24

Noise, air temperature, absolute illumination, relative humidity, radiant heat, negative air ionization and wind velocity were measured at each experimental site. Compared with the city site, the BF sites showed significant differences in temperature, relative humidity, radiant heat, noise, absolute illumination and wind velocity ($p < 0.05$; Table 2).

Table 2. Comparison of the environmental factors of the two environmental sites. Data are presented as the mean ± SEs. CS, city site; BF, bamboo forest sites.

Parameter	CS	BF
Temperature (°C)	28.9 ± 0.26	22.9 ± 1.21
Relative humidity (%)	60.5 ± 2.53	81.1 ± 4.23
Radiant heat (°C)	34.5 ± 0.73	23.1 ± 1.52
Noise (dB)	70.1 ± 0.68	45.6 ± 1.21
Absolute illumination (lux)	6585.7 ± 881	1578.3 ± 623.15
Wind velocity (m/s)	0.9 ± 0.19	0.2 ± 0.13
Negative air ionization (ions/cm^3)	573.3 ± 15.08	962.6 ± 38.97

2.2. Procedures

We chose September for this study, as it is a suitable month for outdoor travel. The weather was sunny during the experimental period. On the afternoon of 19 September, the subjects were divided into four groups. The groups arrived at the arranged hotels near the given experimental sites. The experimental sites were flat areas where the experiment could be easily conducted. The hotels were approximately 300 m from the experimental site. To prevent any effects on emotions, the subjects were allowed to do as they wished in the hotel but were instructed to avoid strenuous exercise and any stimulating activity in their hours of relaxation before sleeping. The experiments of the city site (CS) and bamboo forest sites (BF) were carried out simultaneously. At 08:00 on 20 September 2017 (the first day), psychological and physiological data were taken and blood was sampled. After that, 15 male participants were taken to the city site (CS) and the others were taken to bamboo forest sites (BF). In the next three days, the participants in BF experienced a three-day bamboo forest therapy and the participants in CS were exposed to a city environment. All of the subjects were instructed to remain at their experimental sites from 09:00 to 17:00 except for lunch time. At 8:00 on 23 September 2017 (the fourth day), psychological and physiological data were taken and blood was sampled (see Figure 3).

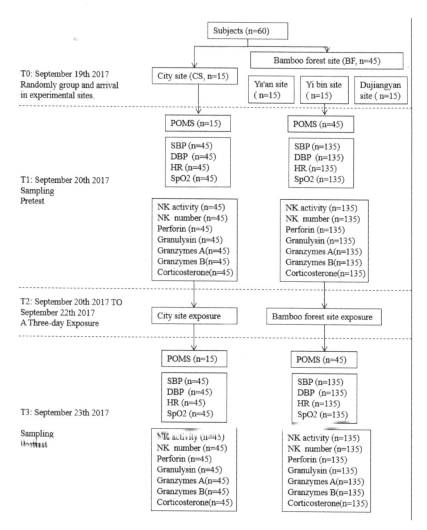

Figure 3. The itinerary for the subjects exposed to the bamboo or urban environment. T0: 19 September 2017; T1: 08:00 on 20 September 2017; T2: 20 September 2017 to 22 September 2017; T3: 08:00 on 23 September 2017.

2.3. Measurement

2.3.1. Psychological Indices

A subjective evaluation of mood was performed using the profile of mood state (POMS) questionnaire. The POMS questionnaire is a well-established, analytically derived measure of psychological distress, and its high levels of reliability and validity have been documented. The POMS questionnaire that we used for the analysis was translated to Chinese by Zhu [29]. For this study, the POMS questionnaire included 30 adjectives rated on a 0–4 scale (i.e., 0, not at all; 1, slightly; 2, moderately; 3, substantially; 4, extremely) that could be consolidated into the following six effective dimensions: tension and anxiety (T-A), depression (T-A), anger and hostility (A-H), fatigue (F), confusion (C), and vigor (V). For T-A, D, A-H, F, and C, a lower score represents a better emotional condition. A higher score for V indicates a better emotional condition. The total mood disturbance (TMD) score was calculated using the following Formula (1) [30], and a total of 120 copies of the POMS questionnaires for the four sites provided the data in this study.

$$\text{TMD score} = (T - A) + (D) + (A - H) + (F) + (C) - (V) \tag{1}$$

2.3.2. Physiological Indices

The physiological indices were measured six times for every participant—three times on the first day and three time on the last day. SBP and DBP were measured with automated BP devices (Omron HEM-7112 Comfort, Omron Health Care (China) Co., Ltd., Dalian, China). BP was measured three times during the intervention, on the left arm with the participants resting in a seated position. Peripheral oxygen saturation (SpO2) was measured with a pulse oximeter (Philips DB18, Philips Medical (Suzhou) Co., Ltd., Suzhou, China) on the index finger of the left hand three times. HR was measured with a single-channel electrocardiograph (Med-ECG-2301, Guangzhou Sanrui Electronic Technology Co., Ltd., Guangzhou, China) three times.

2.3.3. Immune System Indices

Reagents: Roswell Park Memorial Institute (RPMI-1640) medium was purchased from HyClone (Logan, UT, USA). Fetal bovine serum (FBS) was obtained from Clark Bioscience (Richmond, VA, USA). NADI was purchased from Sigma (St. Louis, MO, USA), and nitrotetrazolium blue chloride (NBT) was purchased from Biosharp (Hefei, China). Anti-CD3, anti-CD16, and anti-CD56 were purchased from Biolegend (San Diego, CA, USA). The Human CORT ELISA KIT (XL-Eh0551), Human GNLY ELISA KIT (XL-Eh1850), Human Gzms-A ELISA KIT (XL-Eh1375), Human Gzms-B ELISA KIT (XL-Eh1374), and Human PF T ELISA KIT (XL-Eh0770) were purchased from Abcam (Cambridge, MA, USA).

2.3.4. Sample Preparation

Sterile fresh peripheral blood was collected from the study participants and then preserved at −80 °C after adding heparin anticoagulant. Aseptic absorption of 1 mL of anticoagulant peripheral blood was diluted and mixed with the same amount of culture medium. Then, 5 mL of Ficoll solution was first added to a 15 mL centrifuge tube, and diluted blood was gently added to the upper Ficoll layer of two centrifuge tubes. After centrifugation for 20 min at 2000 rpm, the cells at the junction of the uppermost medium were carefully absorbed, and the separator was added to another aseptic centrifuge tube. Then, 5 mL of PBS was added to the centrifuge tube and centrifuged for 10 min at 1500 rpm. The supernatant was removed and then added to the medium for the same cleaning progress. Finally, the cells were divided into two parts—one for lactate dehydrogenase (LDH) detection and one for flow cytometry staining.

2.3.5. LDH and Cell Number Detection

After resuscitation, passage and cryopreservation of K562 cells (K562 cells were the first human immortalised myelogenous leukemia line to be established), K562 target cells in the logarithmic growth period were centrifuged. The collected cells were washed three times with PBS and centrifuged for 5 min at 800 rpm. The cell density was set to 10^5 for further use. To regulate the concentration of effector monocytes to 10^7, 100 µL of effector cells and target cells was added to a 96-well plate. Two holes were arranged in each specimen, and the target cell natural release control group (target cell K562 + 1640 medium) and maximum release control group (target cell K562 + NP-40) were prepared at the same time. After incubation for 3 h, 0.1 mL of preheated LDH substrate solution was added, followed by a light-avoiding reaction for 15 min at 37 °C and the addition of 30 µL of 1 mol/L citric acid to the solution. The optical density (OD) value was read at a 570 nm wavelength, and NK activity was calculated as follows: (experimental group OD value−natural group OD value)/(largest group

OD value−natural group OD value). The cell numbers were determined by flow cytometry with the default parameters.

2.3.6. ELISA Experiments

Biotin double antibody sandwich enzyme-linked immunosorbent assay (ELISA) was used to determine the levels of corticosterone (CORT), granule lysin (GNLY), granzyme a (Gzms-a), granzyme b (Gzms-B) and perforin (PF). Briefly, the samples to be checked were added to the enzyme-labeled holes, which were precoated with CORT, GNLY, Gzms-A, Gzms-B and PF monoclonal antibody and then incubated. The antibodies against CORT, GNLY, Gzms-A, Gzms-B and PF labeled with biotin were added to bind to streptavidin-HRP to form an immune complex. After incubating and washing, the unbound enzyme was removed, and then substrates A and B were added to generate a blue product, which was converted to final yellow under the action of acid. The depth of color is positively correlated with the concentration of each index in the sample.

Blood was sampled and NK activity was determined; the proportions of NK cells and the levels of granulysin-, corticosterone-, perforin-, and granzyme A/B-expressing cells in PBLs were measured. All measurements were made on the mornings of 20 September and 23 September 2017 at 08:00. All blood samples were placed in an ice/water box at 4 °C, and assays were performed within four hours of the blood draw.

2.4. Statistical Analysis

Because the variability between individuals in the physiological and immune system indices was large, we did not compare the difference in the data between the BF sites and CS locations. Rather, differences in all the data before and after each type of trip were compared in the present study. The BF data were the average of the data from the Ya'an, Yibin and Dujiangyan sites. A paired *t*-test was used to compare the data between pretest and posttest after the three-day bamboo forest therapy session. The Statistical Package for Social Sciences software (v20.0, SPSS Inc., Chicago, IL, USA) was used for all statistical analyses. All data are presented as the means ± standard errors (SEs), and differences were considered significant at $p < 0.05$.

3. Results

3.1. Bamboo Forest Therapy Contributes to the Regulation of Psychological Responses

Scores of negative mood for T-A, D, F, C and A-H at the BF sites significantly decreased after the bamboo forest program ($p < 0.05$; Figure 4a–e). No difference was found in the scores of negative mood for T-A, D, F, C and A-H after the urban program. The scores of V mood significantly increased after the BF program and significantly decreased after the urban program (Figure 4f). In addition, the TMD scores significantly decreased after the bamboo forest program and significantly increased after the urban program (Figure 4g).

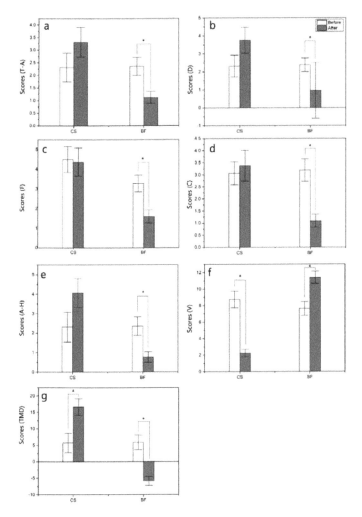

Figure 4. (**a**) tension-anxiety (T-A), (**b**) depression (D), (**c**) fatigue (F), (**d**) confusion (C), (**e**) anger-hostility (A-H), (**f**) vigor (V), (**g**) total mood disturbance TMD. T-scores for tension-anxiety (T-A), depression (D), anger-hostility (A-H), fatigue (F), confusion (C), vigor (V) and total mood disturbance TMD on the profile of mood state (POMS) questionnaire after the bamboo forest and urban programs. A paired *t*-test was used to compare the data between pretest and posttest after the three-day bamboo forest therapy session. The data are presented as the mean ± SEs. * $p < 0.05$, significantly different data between the pretest and posttest for the six mood parameters of the POMS questionnaire by paired t test. CS (n = 15), city site; BF (n = 45), bamboo forest sites.

3.2. Bamboo Forest Therapy Decreases BP in Male College Students

SBP was significantly decreased after the three-day forest bamboo therapy ($p < 0.05$; Figure 5a). At both the CS and BF sites, no significant difference was found between before and after the program in the DBP, HR and SpO2 of male participants (Figure 5b–d). However, the average value of HR was lower at the BF sites and higher at the CS than before the program, although the change was not statistically significant ($p > 0.05$). The results indicated that bamboo forest therapy decreased BP in male college students.

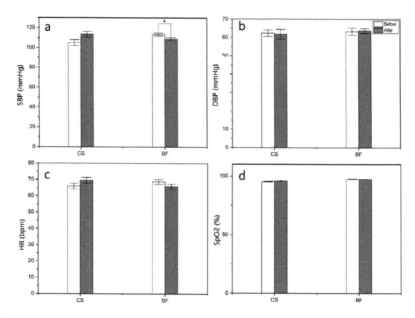

Figure 5. (**a**) systolic blood pressure (SBP), (**b**) diastolic blood pressure (DBP), (**c**) heart rate (HR), (**d**) peripheral oxygen saturation (SpO2). Comparison of systolic blood pressure, diastolic blood pressure, heart rate and peripheral oxygen saturation in participants after the bamboo forest and urban program. A paired *t*-test was used to compare the data between pretest and posttest after the three-day bamboo forest therapy session. The data are presented as the mean ± SEs. * $p < 0.05$, significantly different data between the pretest and posttest for the physiological indices by paired t test. CS (n = 15), city site; BF (n = 45), bamboo forest sites. SBP, systolic blood pressure; DBP, diastolic blood pressure; HR, heart rate; SpO2, peripheral oxygen saturation.

3.3. Bamboo Forest Therapy Enhances the Immune Response in Male College Students

Compared with the pretest values, NK activity, the number of NK cells, and the levels of perforin, granzyme A and granzyme B in the PBLs of participants were significantly increased after the BF program ($p < 0.05$; Figure 6a–f). Corticosterone in PBLs was significantly decreased after the BF program (Figure 6g). For the CS program, no significant difference was found in NK activity, the number of NK cells, or the levels of perforin, granulysin, corticosterone, granzyme A and granzyme B in PBLs. In addition, no significant difference was found in granulysin in PBLs with the BF program.

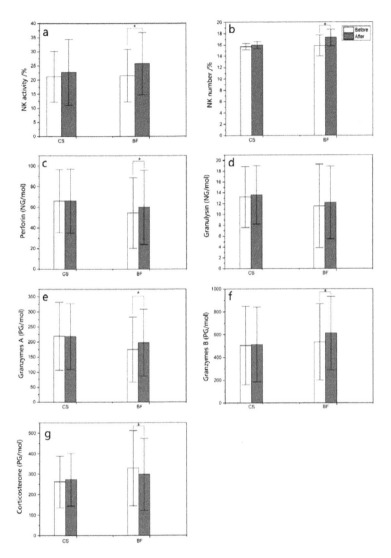

Figure 6. (**a**) NK activity), (**b**) the number of NK cells, (**c**) perforin, (**d**) granulysin, (**e**) granzyme A, (**f**) granzyme B, (**g**) corticosterone. Comparison of NK activity, the number of NK cells, perforin-, granulysin-, granzyme A/B- and corticosterone-expressing cells in peripheral blood lymphocytes in participants after the bamboo forest and urban programs. A paired *t*-test was used to compare the data between pretest and posttest after the three-day bamboo forest therapy session. The data are presented as the mean ± SEs. * $p < 0.05$, significantly different data between the pretest and posttest for the parameters by paired t test. CS (n = 15), city site; BF (n = 45), bamboo forest sites.

4. Discussion

This study investigated the psychological, physiological and immune system effects of a three-day BF therapy on male college students, as well as the difference in these effects before and after the three-day BF therapy.

The present study confirmed that the three-day therapy session in the BF enhanced positive mood states and reduced negative mood states. A previous study reported that forest environments improve psychological well-being [20,21]. Furthermore, the literature has also reported that forest therapy can reduce negative psychological symptoms and increase positive mood states [3,23], which was consistent with our results for the psychological response to BF therapy.

Physiological data from this field experiment showed that the SBP was significantly lower in participants after a three-day BF therapy session. The DBP and HR exhibited the same trend as SBP, but the change was not statistically significant. The SpO2 of participants was higher after the BF program than before the program. However, no difference in physiological indices was found between pretest and posttest with the urban program. Previous studies have also shown that the mean HR was significantly lower when participants viewed a forest area than when they viewed an urban area [23,31–33]. The present result on the physiological benefits of BF therapy is partly consistent with the previous study. BP is one of the vital signs, along with respiratory rate, HR, SpO2, and body temperature. Normal resting BP in an adult is approximately 120 mm of mercury systolic and 80 mm of mercury diastolic. SpO2 is the fraction of oxygen-saturated hemoglobin relative to total hemoglobin in blood. Normal blood oxygen levels in humans are considered 95%–100%. Given the probable differences between individuals, the decrease in DBP and HR and the increase in SpO2 between the pretest and posttest measurements were not statistically significant. However, despite these differences between individuals, it seems that there is a relatively clear tendency showing the beneficial effects of BF therapy sessions compared with urban environment sessions on the physiological response of male college students.

The present study provided evidence for strengthening of the immune system in male college students after a three-day BF therapy session. The results of a paired *t*-test comparing the pretest and posttest conditions showed a significant increase in NK activity, the number of NK cells, and the levels of perforin and granzymes A/B in lymphocytes and a significant decrease in corticosterone in the blood samples. Recent field studies on forest bathing have provided interesting scientific data indicating that forest bathing trips significantly increased NK activity, the number of NK cells, and the levels of perforin, granulysin, and granzymes A/B in PBLs, and the increased NK activity lasted for more than 7 days after the trip [24–26]. Other studies have shown that participants in a two day forest therapy session showed a significantly larger increase in NK cell activity than participants in the control group [34]. In addition, a forest bathing trip can increase NK activity, and this effect is at least partially mediated by increasing the number of NK cells and by the induction of intracellular anticancer proteins. However, no significant difference was found between pretest and posttest in the urban program in NK activity, the number of NK cells, the levels of granulysin, perforin, granzymes A/B in lymphocytes, or corticosterone levels. NK cells are a sub-population of lymphocytes that are able to recognize and lyse a wide variety of target cells [35]. NK cells are recognized as a separate lymphocyte lineage, with both cytotoxicity and cytokine-producing effector functions [36]. Recent studies continue to confirm the importance of NK cells for host resistance, particularly against tumor metastasis [37] and against infection by certain viruses [38]. One mechanism for NK cells to induce tumor- or virus-infected target cell death involves granule exocytosis, with the direct release of cytolytic granules containing perforin, granzymes and granulysin that kill target cells via apoptosis [39]. The increase in the number of NK cells and perforin-, granulysin-, and granzyme A/B-expressing cells in PBLs represents benefits for humans [24]. Therefore, bamboo forest therapy enhances the immune function of male college students by increasing NK activity, the number of NK cells and the levels of intracellular granulysin, perforin, and granzymes A/B in PBLs.

BF therapy can improve the psychological and physiological well-being and enhance the immune functions of male college students. However, the mechanism underlying the benefits to the psycho-physiological and immune systems after BF therapy is unclear.

First, according to biophilia and human evolutionary theories [40,41], the result may be partly explained by the fact that humans have spent many thousands of years adapting to the natural environment and possess an innate tendency to seek connections with the natural environment and other forms of life. According to Kaplan's [42] "Attention restoration theory," an environment that possesses a restorative effect requires four properties: being away, fascination, extent, and compatibility [33]. Consequently, Kaplan argued that natural environments are ideal places to restore diminished attentional capacity and provide these elements. In accordance with these theories, a BF is a restorative environment that may improve the psychological and physiological well-being of people.

Second, aromatic volatile substances (phytoncides) extracted from trees may play an important role in the recovery of the immune system. Many studies have shown the meaningful physiological effects of a forest atmosphere on people [17,43,44]. In addition, floral scents can improve mood states and may lead to improvements in emotional health, depression, and memory disorders [45]. These effects are believed to be achieved by inhaling the forest atmosphere, which includes various phytochemicals mainly produced by trees. Li et al. measured NK activity, the percentages of NK and T-cells, and the levels of granulysin-, perforin-, and granzyme A/B-expressing lymphocytes in the blood of participants who were exposed to a room containing many phytoncides produced by vaporizing *Chamaecyparis obtusa* (hinoki cypress) stem oil [46]. Phytoncides, such as α-pinene, β-pinene, β-cadinene, and limonene, were detected in the hotel room air during the experiment. The results showed that phytoncides from trees can increase NK activity, the number of NK cells, and the expression of intracellular perforin and granzyme A/B in male subjects. In addition, essential oils derived from various plants have neuroprotective effects against neurodegenerative conditions in vivo and in vitro [47]. Other studies have also shown that alcohols, acids, alkanes, phenols, and ketones are the main aromatic volatile substances in the BF environment [48,49]. Therefore, phytoncides in BF air may partially contribute to the increased NK activity, the number of NK cells, and expression of intracellular perforin and granzyme A/B in subjects after a three-day BF therapy session.

Third, in addition to the phytoncides, the physical environments at BF sites that differ from the environment at the CS may affect the benefits in participants who experienced a three-day therapy program. A beneficial environment such as a forest, which should include diverse vegetation and ecological components, helps improve the effect of a psychotherapeutic intervention [50,51]. In addition, a five-senses experience from walking or staying in a forest was reported to relieve stress and thus yield health benefits [43]. Additionally, there has been little research on the effects of physical environments on the immune system. Exposure to high concentrations of atmospheric particulate matter, noise and ultraviolet light for a long time is not beneficial for the immune system of humans. However, the urban environment possesses characteristics that are unnatural, unhealthy, uncomfortable, too bright and noisy [19]. In the present study, the absolute illumination at the BF site was significantly lower than that at the CS location. The temperature at the BF site was close to 25 °C, which is a more suitable temperature for humans than the temperatures at the CS location. The noise level at the BF sites was significantly lower than that at the CS location. Based on our field investigation, the environment at the BF sites was significantly different from that at the CS location in terms of absolute illumination, temperature, noise and negative air ionization. Therefore, the physical environments in the BF may induce psycho-physiological relaxation and immune system recovery.

Fourth, the cultural conceptions about bamboo may be an explanation for the positive effects on psychological and physiological responses after a three-day BF therapy session. Mental health and culture are intertwined, and culture is a great determinant of mental well-being and psycho-pathological state. Culture also influences the cause, perception, symptomatology, course, health-seeking behavior and treatment of mental illness [52]. Studies have demonstrated that adaptation to culturally characterized visual environments may lead to distinct patterns of perception [53]. Bamboo culture has a long history and is well known in East and Southeast Asia and in African countries. Bamboo-derived objects are prevalent among people living in bamboo-growing areas, and people have developed a special attachment to bamboo, which has developed into a bamboo culture. In our study, participants who viewed the landscape of BF presented positive patterns of perception that were influenced by bamboo culture.

Evidence-based research has clarified the benefits of forest therapy on psychophysiology and the immune system. However, the mechanism underlying the benefits in participants after a three-day bamboo forest therapy were not clear. Actually, there are complex interactions and exchanges of biologically active molecules between the nervous, endocrine and immune systems. Pathways between the brain and the immune system are bidirectional [54]. Two pathways link the brain and the immune system: the autonomic nervous system and neuroendocrine outflow via the pituitary. The central nervous system (CNS) can communicate with the immune system following activation of the hypothalamic–pituitary–adrenal (HPA) axis and the sympathetic nervous system (SNS). All immunoregulatory processes take place within a neuroendocrine environment that is sensitive to the influence of the individual's perception of and response to events in the external world. Because lymphocytes bear receptors for various hormones and neuropeptides, the cellular interactions that mediate humoral and cellular immune responses can be modulated by the neuroendocrine environment in which these immune responses occur. In addition, a striking example of CNS involvement in the modulation of immunity is the Pavlovian response, which is a classical conditioning of antibody- and cell-mediated immune responses [55]. Therefore, the interactions between the nervous, endocrine and immune systems could explain the psychophysiology and the immune system responses in participants after a three-day BF therapy session (Figure 7).

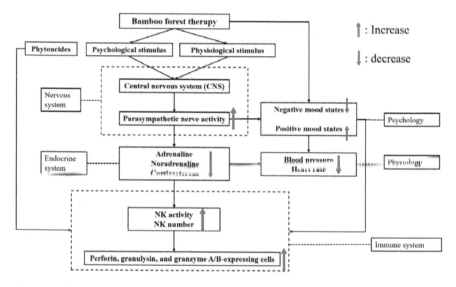

Figure 7. The mechanism of interactions between the nervous, endocrine and immune systems in participants after a three-day bamboo forest therapy.

Participants were stimulated by the BF environment both psychologically and physiologically. First, the CNS, including the brainstem, had increased parasympathetic nerve activity and suppressed sympathetic nerve activity by neuropeptides after the stimulus of BF therapy [32,56]. The effects on the parasympathetic nervous system could include a reduction in HR, improvements in heart rate variability and baroreflex sensitivity parameters, changes in cytokine expression, or other electrophysiological or central modulations [57]. For forest stimuli, the resulting elevated parasympathetic nervous activity, which is usually observed under conditions of relaxation, indicates that forest bathing may facilitate physiological relaxation [56,58]. In the present study, the decrease in BP, HR, and score of negative mood state may be caused by the activity of the parasympathetic nervous system. The parasympathetic nervous system is also associated with decreases in blood levels of adrenaline, noradrenaline and corticosterone via hormones secreted from the pituitary gland [54]. The levels of corticosterone in PBLs were significantly lower after the three-day BF therapy session but not after the urban program in this study. Forest bathing trips were shown to significantly decrease urine adrenaline and noradrenaline concentrations in males with lower stress [59]. Alternatively, neuroendocrine factors may modulate the immune response indirectly by affecting the production of lymphokines and monokines [60]. Reports indicated that adrenaline and noradrenaline inhibit human NK activity [61,62]. In addition, physical and/or psychological stress decreases NK activity, NK receptor levels, and mRNA transcription levels of granzymes and perforin in mice [63]. Additionally, psychological states are related to the immune system, such that a good psychological condition in participants enhances immunity [64]. Therefore, the improvement in the immune system may be caused by a decrease in adrenaline and noradrenaline concentrations and a positive psychological condition. The increase in parasympathetic nerve activity after a three-day BF therapy session resulted in low levels of adrenaline and noradrenaline and psychological and physiological relaxation. In the urban program, no significant difference in psychophysiological and immune system responses was found between pretest and posttest data in participants.

5. Conclusions

A three-day BF therapy session was capable of enhancing positive mood states and reducing negative mood states in male college students. The BP and HR of male college students were decreased, and SpO2 was increased after a three-day BF therapy session. BF therapy significantly increased NK activity, the number of NK cells, and the levels of perforin, granulysin, and granzymes A/B in PBLs in male college students. In summary, a three-day BF therapy session can improve the psychological and physiological well-being and enhance the immune functions of male college students. First, the stimulation of BF therapy increased parasympathetic nerve activity and suppressed sympathetic nerve activity in participants. Then, the concentrations of adrenaline, noradrenaline and corticosterone in the PBLs of participants and stress were reduced after the increase in parasympathetic nerve activity. Finally, a decrease in adrenaline and noradrenaline concentrations and a positive effect on psychology may lead to an increase in NK activity, the number of NK cells, and the levels of perforin, granulysin, and granzymes A/B in PBL.

This study is the first to research the benefits of a three-day bamboo forest therapy session on the psychophysiology and immune system responses of male college students. We gave an explanation of the mechanism underlying the benefits in humans and the interactions between the nervous, endocrine and immune systems in participants after a three-day bamboo forest therapy. However, the study has limitations. A small sample size may be the limitation for the data statistics. Individual differences are also a difficult problem to address. While the benefits of bamboo forest therapy to college students was obvious, aromatic volatile substances (phytoncides) extracted from bamboo forests should be tested. The inclusion of a larger number of participants in this experiment would have produced more scientific and objective results. Further studies with larger samples, including subjects with illnesses such as cardiovascular disease, hypertension and cancer, are warranted.

Author Contributions: Conceptualization, B.L., M.J. and Q.C.; Data curation, W.L.; Formal analysis, B.L. and D.L.; Funding acquisition, Q.C.; Investigation, B.L., C.Z., S.X. and N.L.; Methodology, C.Z.; Project administration, B.L., M.J. and Q.C.; Software, C.Z. and S.X.; Supervision, D.L. and M.J.; Validation, D.L. and S.L.; Visualization, W.L., N.L. and S.L.; Writing–original draft, B.L.; Writing–review & editing, S.L. and Q.C.

Funding: National Key R&D Program of China (No. 2018YFD0600105).

Acknowledgments: This study was financially supported by the National Key R&D Program of China (No. 2018YFD0600105). We thank the professional editing service company (American Journal Experts) for their assistance in reviewing the English language of the manuscript.

Conflicts of Interest: The authors declare no conflict of interest.

References

1. Lee, I.; Choi, H.; Bang, K.; Kim, S.; Song, M.; Lee, B. Effects of forest therapy on depressive symptoms among adults: A systematic review. *Int. J. Environ. Res. Public Health* **2017**, *14*, 321. [CrossRef] [PubMed]

2. Staats, H.; Jahncke, H.; Herzog, T.R.; Hartig, T. Urban options for psychological restoration: Common strategies in everyday situations. *PLoS ONE* **2016**, *11*, e0146213. [CrossRef] [PubMed]

3. Yu, C.P.; Lin, C.M.; Tsai, M.J.; Tsai, Y.C.; Chen, C.Y. Effects of short forest bathing program on autonomic nervous system activity and mood states in middle-aged and elderly individuals. *Int. J. Environ. Res. Public Health* **2017**, *14*, 897. [CrossRef] [PubMed]

4. Sifferlin, A. The healing power of nature. *Time* **2016**, *7*, 23–26.

5. Lu, R.S. World Health Report of 2007. *J. Med. Inform.* **2007**, *6*, 637–638.

6. Eisenberg, D.; Gollust, S.E.; Golberstein, E.; Hefner, J.L. Prevalence and correlates of depression, anxiety, and suicidality among university students. *Am. J. Orthopsychiatr.* **2007**, *77*, 534–542. [CrossRef]

7. Regehr, C.; Glancy, D.; Pitts, A. Interventions to reduce stress in university students: A review and meta-analysis. *J. Affect. Disord.* **2013**, *148*, 1–11. [CrossRef]

8. Frumkin, H. Beyond toxicity human health and the natural environment. *Am. J. Prev. Med.* **2001**, *20*, 234–240. [CrossRef]

9. UN-Habitat. State of the World's Cities: Bridging the Urban Divide. Available online: http://www.unhabitat.org/documents/SOWC10/R7.pdf (accessed on 1 June 2011).

10. Williams, F. This is your brain on nature. *Natl. Geogr.* **2016**, *229*, 48–69.

11. Hartig, T.; Evans, G.W.; Jamner, L.D.; Davis, D.S.; Gärling, T. Tracking restoration in natural and urban field settings. *J. Environ. Psychol.* **2003**, *23*, 109–123. [CrossRef]

12. Laumann, K.; Gärling, T.; Stormark, K.M. Selective attention and heart rate responses to natural and urban environments. *J. Environ. Psychol.* **2003**, *23*, 125–134. [CrossRef]

13. Morita, E.; Fukuda, S.; Nagano, J.; Hamajima, N.; Yamamoto, H.; Iwai, Y.; Nakashima, T.; Ohira, H.; Shirakawa, T. Psychological effects of forest environments on healthy adults: Shinrin-yoku (forest-air bathing, walking) as a possible method of stress reduction. *Public Health* **2007**, *121*, 54–63. [CrossRef] [PubMed]

14. Berg, A.E.; Maas, J.; Verheij, R.A.; Groenewegen, P.P. Green space as a buffer between stressful life events and health. *Soc. Sci. Med.* **2010**, *70*, 1203–1210. [CrossRef] [PubMed]

15. Horiuchi, M.; Endo, J.; Takayama, N.; Murase, K.; Nishiyama, N.; Saito, H.; Fujiwara, A. Impact of viewing vs. Not viewing a real forest on physiological and psychological responses in the same setting. *Int. J. Environ. Res. Public Health* **2011**, *11*, 10883–10901. [CrossRef] [PubMed]

16. Karjalainen, E.; Sarjala, T.; Raitio, H. Promoting human health through forests: Overview and major challenges. *Environ. Health Prev. Med.* **2010**, *15*, 1–8. [CrossRef]

17. Park, B.J.; Tsunetsugu, Y.; Kasetani, T.; Kagawa, T.; Miyazaki, Y. The physiological effects of Shinrin-yoku (taking in the forest atmosphere or forest bathing): Evidence from field experiments in 24 forests across Japan. *Environ. Health Prev. Med.* **2010**, *15*, 18–26. [CrossRef]

18. Tsunetsugu, Y.; Park, B.J.; Ishii, H.; Hirano, H.; Kagawa, T.; Miyazaki, Y. Physiological effects of Shinrin-yoku (taking in the atmosphere of the forest) in an old-growth broadleaf forest in Yamagata Prefecture, Japan. *J. Physiol. Anthropol.* **2007**, *26*, 135–142. [CrossRef]

19. Song, C.; Lee, J.; Ikei, H.; Kagawa, T.; Miyazaki, Y.; Park, B.-J. Physiological and psychological effects of walking around and viewing a lake in a forest environment. *J. Korean For. Soc.* **2015**, *104*, 140–149. [CrossRef]

20. Herzog, T.R.; Black, A.M.; Fountaine, K.A.; Knotts, D.J. Reflection and attentional recovery as two distinctive benefits of restorative environments. *J. Environ. Psychol.* **1997**, *17*, 165–170. [CrossRef]

21. Kaplan, R. The nature of the view from home: Psychological benefits. *Environ. Behav.* **2001**, *33*, 507–542. [CrossRef]

22. Joung, D.; Kim, G.; Choi, Y.; Lim, H.; Park, S.; Woo, J.; Park, B. The Prefrontal Cortex Activity and Psychological Effects of Viewing Forest Landscapes in Autumn Season. *Int. J. Environ. Res. Public Health* **2015**, *12*, 7235–7243. [CrossRef] [PubMed]

23. Lee, J.; Tsunetsugu, Y.; Takayama, N.; Park, B.J.; Li, Q.; Song, C.; Komatsu, M.; Ikei, H.; Tyrväinen, L.; Kagawa, T.; et al. Influence of forest therapy on cardiovascular relaxation in young adults. *Evid. Based Complement Alternat. Med.* **2014**, *2014*, 834360. [CrossRef] [PubMed]

24. Li, Q.; Morimoto, K.; Nakadai, A.; Inagaki, H.; Katsumata, M.; Shimizu, T.; Hirata, Y.; Hirata, K.; Suzuki, H.; Miyazaki, Y. Forest bathing enhances human natural killer activity and expression of anti-cancer proteins. *Int. J. Immunopathol. Pharmacol.* **2007**, *20*, 3–8. [CrossRef] [PubMed]

25. Li, Q.; Morimoto, K.; Kobayashi, M.; Inagaki, H.; Katsumata, M.; Hirata, Y.; Hirata, K.; Shimizu, T.; Li, Y.; Wakayama, Y. A forest bathing trip increases human natural killer activity and expression of anti-cancer proteins in female subjects. *J. Biol. Regul. Homeost. Agents* **2008**, *22*, 45–55. [PubMed]

26. Li, Q.; Kobayashi, M.; Inagaki, H.; Hirata, Y.; Li, Y.; Hirata, K.; Shimizu, T.; Suzuki, H.; Katsumata, M.; Wakayama, Y. A day trip to a forest park increases human natural killer activity and the expression of anti-cancer proteins in male subjects. *J. Biol. Regul. Homeost. Agents* **2010**, *24*, 157–165. [PubMed]

27. Zhou, B.Z.; Fu, M.Y.; Xie, J.Z.; Yang, X.S.; Li, Z.C. Ecological functions of bamboo forest: Research and Application. *For. Res.* **2005**, *16*, 143–147.

28. Liu, S.L.; Yang, R.J.; Yang, R.J.; Yi, T.P.; Song, H.X.; Jiang, M.Y.; Tripathi, D.K.; Ma, M.D.; Chen, Q.B. Differentiating Thamnocalamus Munro from *Fargesia Franchet* emend. Yi (Bambusoideae, Poaceae): Novel evidence from morphological and neural-network analyses. *Sci. Rep.* **2017**, *7*, 4192. [CrossRef]

29. Zhu, B.L. Brief introduction of POMS scale and its model for China. *J. Tianjin Inst. Phys. Educ.* **1995**, *10*, 35–37.

30. McNair, D.M.; Lorr, M.; Droppleman, L.F. *Profile of Mood States*; Revised; EdITS/Educational and Industrial Testing Service: San Diego, CA, USA, 1992.

31. Mao, G.X.; Cao, Y.B.; Lan, X.G.; He, Z.H.; Chen, Z.M.; Wang, Y.Z.; Hu, X.L.; Lv, Y.D.; Wang, G.F.; Yan, J. Therapeutic effect of forest bathing on human hypertension in the elderly. *J. Cardiol.* **2012**, *60*, 495–502. [CrossRef]

32. Tsunetsugu, Y.; Lee, J.; Park, B.J.; Tyrväinen, L.; Kagawa, T.; Miyazaki, Y. Physiological and psychological effects of viewing urban forest landscapes assessed by multiple measurements. *Landsc. Urban Plan.* **2013**, *113*, 90–93. [CrossRef]

33. Song, C.; Ikei, H.; Kobayashi, M.; Miura, T.; Li, Q.; Kagawa, T.; Kumeda, S.; o Imai, M.; Miyazaki, Y. Effects of viewing forest landscape on middle-aged hypertensive men. *Urban For. Urban Green.* **2017**, *21*, 247–252. [CrossRef]

34. Han, J.W.; Choi, H.; Jeon, Y.H.; Yoon, C.H.; Woo, J.M.; Kim, W. The effects of forest therapy on coping with chronic widespread pain: Physiological and psychological differences between participants in a forest therapy program and a control group. *Int. J. Environ. Res. Public Health* **2016**, *13*, 255. [CrossRef] [PubMed]

35. Herberman, R.B. Natural killer cells. *Ann. Rev. Med.* **1986**, *37*, 347–352. [CrossRef] [PubMed]

36. Vivier, E.; Tomasello, E.; Baratin, M.; Walzer, T.; Ugolini, S. Functions of natural killer cells. *Nat. Immunol.* **2008**, *9*, 503–510. [CrossRef]

37. Barlozzari, T.; Leonhardt, J.; Wiltrout, R.; Herberman, R.B.; Reynolds, C.W. Direct evidence for the role of LGL in the inhibition of experimental tumor metastases. *J. Immunol.* **1985**, *134*, 2783–2789.

38. Bukowski, J.F.; Woda, B.A.; Habu, S.; Okumura, K.; Welsh, R.M. Natural killer cell depletion enhances virus synthesis and virus-induced hepatitis in vivo. *J. Immunol.* **1983**, *131*, 1531–1538.

39. Li, Q.; Morimoto, K.; Nakadai, A.; Qu, T.L.; Matsushima, H.; Katsumata, M.; Shimizu, T.; Inagaki, H.; Hirata, Y.; Hirata, K.; et al. Healthy lifestyles are associated with higher levels of perforin, granulysin and granzymes A/B-expressing cells in peripheral blood lymphocytes. *Prev. Med.* **2007**, *44*, 117–123. [CrossRef]

40. Wilson, E.O. *Biophilia: The Human Bond with Other Species*; Harvard University Press: Cambridge, UK, 1984.

41. Ulrich, R.S.; Addoms, D.L. Psychological and Recreational Benefits of a Residential Park. *J. Leis. Res.* **1981**, *13*, 43–65. [CrossRef]

42. Kaplan, S. Journal of the restorative benefits of nature: Towards an integrative framework. *Environ. Psychol.* **1995**, *1*, 169–182. [CrossRef]

43. Tsunetsugu, Y.; Park, B.J.; Miyazaki, Y. Trends in research related to 'Shinrin-yoku' (taking in the forest atmosphere or forest bathing) in Japan. *Environ. Health Prev. Med.* **2010**, *15*, 27–37. [CrossRef]

44. Song, C.; Ikei, H.; Miyazaki, Y. Physiological Effects of Nature Therapy: A Review of the Research in Japan. *Int. J. Environ. Res. Public Health* **2016**, *13*, 781. [CrossRef] [PubMed]

45. Jo, H.; Rodiek, S.; Fujii, E.; Miyazaki, Y.; Park, B.J.; Ann, S.W. Physiological and psychological response to floral scent. *Hortscience* **2013**, *48*, 82–88. [CrossRef]

46. Li, Q.; Kobayashi, M.; Wakayama, Y.; Inagaki, H.; Katsumata, M.; Hirata, Y.; Hirata, K.; Shimizu, T.; Kawada, T.; Park, J.; et al. Effect of phytoncide from trees on human natural killer cell function. *Int. J. Immunopathol. Pharmacol.* **2009**, *22*, 951–959. [CrossRef] [PubMed]

47. Cho, K.S.; Lim, Y.R.; Lee, K.; Lee, J.; Lee, J.H.; Lee, I.S. Terpenes from forests and human health. *Toxicol. Res.* **2017**, *33*, 97–106. [CrossRef]

48. Zhang, Y.; Tang, J. Research of aromatic volatile substances on bamboo leaves. *Natl. Prod. Res. Dev.* **1998**, *10*, 38–44.

49. Yang, P.; Liu, H.B.; Pan, J.J.; Chen, D.M. Comparative study on volatile oil composition and antibacterial activity of bamboo leaves in different seasons. *J. Nucl. Agric. Sci.* **2015**, *2*, 313–320.

50. Kim, W.; Lim, S.; Chung, E.; Woo, J. The Effect of Cognitive Behavior Therapy-Based Psychotherapy Applied in a Forest Environment on Physiological Changes and Remission of Major Depressive Disorder. *Psychiatry Investig.* **2009**, *6*, 245–254. [CrossRef]

51. Stigsdotter, U.K.; Corazon, S.S.; Sidenius, U.; Refshauge, A.D.; Grahn, P. Forest design for mental health promotion-Using perceived sensory dimensions to elicit restorative responses. *Landsc. Urban Plan.* **2017**, *160*, 1–15. [CrossRef]

52. Omigbodun, O.; Oyebode, F. *Contemporary Issues in Mental Health Care in Sub-Saharan Africa*; BookBuilders Editions Africa: Port Harcourt, Nigeria, 2017; pp. 203–204.

53. Park, I.; Hong, Y. Culture and sensory response to visual stimuli. *Int. J. Psychol.* **2018**, *53*, 77–81. [CrossRef]

54. Ader, R.; Cohen, N.; Felten, D. Psychoneuroimmunology: Interactions between the nervous system and the immune system. *Lancet* **1995**, *345*, 99–103. [CrossRef]

55. Ader, R.; Cohen, N.; Felten, D.L. The influence of conditioning on immune responses. In *Psychoneuroimmunology*, 2nd ed.; Academic: New York, NY, USA, 1991; pp. 611–646.

56. Lee, J.; Park, B.J.; Tsunetsugu, Y.; Ohira, T.; Kagawa, T.; Miyazaki, Y. Effect of forest bathing on physiological and psychological responses in young Japanese male subjects. *Public Health* **2011**, *125*, 93–100. [CrossRef] [PubMed]

57. Olshansky, B.; Sabbah, H.N.; Hauptman, P.J.; Colucci, W.S. Parasympathetic nervous system and heart failure pathophysiology and potential implications for therapy. *Circulation* **2008**, *118*, 863–871. [CrossRef]

58. Yamaguchi, M.; Deguchi, M.; Miyazaki, Y. The effects of exercise in forest and urban environments on sympathetic nervous activity of normal young adults. *J. Int. Med. Res.* **2006**, *34*, 152–159. [CrossRef]

59. Li, Q.; Morimoto, K.; Kobayashi, M.; Inagaki, H.; Katsumata, M.; Hirata, Y.; Hirata, K.; Suzuki, H.; Li, Y.J.; Wakayama, Y. Visiting a forest, but not a city, increases human natural killer activity and expression of anti-cancer proteins. *Int. J. Immunopathol. Pharmacol.* **2008**, *21*, 117–127. [CrossRef]

60. DeRijk, R.; Berkenbosch, F. The immune–hypothalamo–pituitary–adrenal axis and autoimmunity. *Int. J. Neurosci.* **1991**, *59*, 91–100. [CrossRef]

61. Garland, M.; Doherty, D.; Golden-Mason, L.; Fitzpatrick, P.; Walsh, N.; O'Farrelly, C. Stress-related hormonal suppression of natural killer activity does not show menstrual cycle variations: Implications for timing of surgery for breast cancer. *Anticancer Res.* **2003**, *23*, 2531–2535.

62. Yokota, T.; Uehara, K.; Nomoto, Y. Addition of noradrenaline to intrathecal morphine augments the postoperative suppression of natural killer cell activity. *J. Anesth.* **2004**, *18*, 190–195. [CrossRef]

63. Li, Q.; Liang, Z.; Nakadai, A.; Kawada, T. Effect of electric foot shock and psychological stress on activities of murine splenic natural killer and lymphokine-activated killer cells, cytotoxic T lymphocytes, natural killer receptors and mRNA transcripts for granzymes and perforin. *Stress* **2005**, *8*, 107–116. [CrossRef]

64. Sun, X.L. The influence of psychological factors on the human immune system. *J. Psychol.* **1998**, *2*, 11–17.

International Journal of
Environmental Research and Public Health

Communication

Can Exposure to Certain Urban Green Spaces Trigger Frontal Alpha Asymmetry in the Brain?—Preliminary Findings from a Passive Task EEG Study

Agnieszka Olszewska-Guizzo [1,2,*], Angelia Sia [3], Anna Fogel [4] and Roger Ho [1,5]

1   Institute for Health Innovation & Technology (iHealthtech) MD6, 14 Medical Drive, #14-01, Singapore 117599, Singapore; pcmrhcm@nus.edu.sg
2   NeuroLandscape Foundation, Suwalska 8/78, 03-252 Warsaw, Poland
3   National Parks Board, Centre for Urban Greenery and Ecology, 1E Cluny Road Singapore Botanic Gardens, Singapore 259601, Singapore; ANGELIA_SIA@nparks.gov.sg
4   Singapore Institute for Clinical Sciences, Agency for Science, Technology and Research, 12 Science Drive 2, Tahir Foundation Building #12, Singapore 117549, Singapore; Anna_Fogel@sics.a-star.edu.sg
5   Department of Psychological Medicine, Yong Loo Lin School of Medicine, the National University of Singapore, NUHS Tower Block, Level 9 1E Kent Ridge Road, Singapore 119228, Singapore
*   Correspondence: aga@nus.edu.sg or olszewska.agn@gmail.com; Tel.: +65-914-08707

Received: 29 November 2019; Accepted: 3 January 2020; Published: 7 January 2020

Abstract: A growing body of evidence from observational and experimental studies shows the associations between exposure to urban green spaces (UGSs) and mental health outcomes. Little is known about which specific features of UGS that might be the most beneficial. In addition, there is potential in utilizing objective physiological markers of mental health, such as assessing brain activity, but the subject requires further investigation. This paper presents the preliminary findings from an on-going within-subject experiment where adult participants ($n = 22$; 13 females) were passively exposed to six landscape scenes within two UGSs (a park and a neighborhood green space) and three scenes of a busy urban downtown (control site). The landscape scenes were pre-selected based on their contemplative landscape score (CLS) to represent different levels of aggregation of contemplative features within each view. Participants went to each of the sites in a random order to passively view the scenes, while their electroencephalography (EEG) signal was being recorded concurrently. Frontal alpha asymmetry (FAA) values, commonly associated with the approach-related motivation and positive emotions, were extracted. The preliminary results show trends for the main effect of site on FAA, suggestive of stronger FAA in park compared to the control site, akin to more positive mood. There was also a trend for the interaction between the site and scene, which suggests that even within the individual sites, there is variability depending on the specific scene. Adjusting for environmental covariate strengthened these effects, these interim findings are promising in supporting the study hypothesis and suggest that exposure to urban green spaces may be linked to mental health outcomes.

Keywords: urban; landscape; brain; visual; green; contemplative; mental health; well-being; FAA; EEG; UGS; depression

1. Introduction

Environmental exposures are a sum of all sensory stimuli we receive along the life cycle, closely intertwined with our mental health and well-being (MH&WB) [1,2]. As visual stimuli provide the most information about the environment around us [3], the visual quality of scenes we are exposed to seems worth investigating. This is even more so if we consider a rapidly urbanizing world where most people already live in cities [4].

Urbanized areas are characterized by the concentration of built elements and infrastructure, crowdedness, noise and pollution. Visually, the urbanized environment is highly transformed from its natural manifestation. Potential negative effects of the urban visual exposures on MH&WB have been already noted by Sir Fredrick Law Olmsted, the front runner of American sanitary reform in early XIX century, known as the Father of Landscape Architecture: "A man's eyes cannot be as much occupied as they are in large cities by artificial things ... without harmful effect, first on his mental and nervous system and ultimately on his entire constitutional organization" [5]. Recent meta-analysis seems to confirm these words with scientific evidence, demonstrating the 38% higher prevalence rate of mental health disorders in urban when compared to rural areas, with mood disorders, such as major depressive disorder (MDD) causing a major burden [6,7].

Therefore, urban green spaces (UGSs) play a major role in mitigating the negative effects of urban environment exposures on MH&WB. There is an established consensus among researchers that contact with natural environments has beneficial influence on MH&WB of people [8–16]. However, most studies are based on a vague comparison between "urban" versus "nature" exposure, while more specific elements and attributes of UGS, and their composition have not been, to date, identified. Moreover, the knowledge in this area is based mostly on the correlational analyses, and more rigorous experimental approached are needed to examine causal relationships between specific environmental features and mental health that will form the basis of future urban landscape design. There is a need to identify which specific types of the natural environments found in cities have the most beneficial effects on people's MH&WB. Moreover, there is a need to assess these effects through rigorous experimental designs, with the use of objective tools and objective markers of mental health in order to examine causality.

1.1. Frontal Alpha Asymmetry and Mental Health

FAA is one of the most studied brainwave patterns that is an objective measure of current mood. It is associated with an increased alpha power in the right frontal lobe when compared to the left. As in brain science more alpha power indicates less activation, FAA can be also referred to as decreased activation of the right frontal lobe when compared to the left. According to the approach-withdrawal hypothesis [17] FAA is associated with the appetitive motivational system towards the perceived stimulus and positive emotions (e.g., happiness and calmness), while the pattern opposite to FAA is associated with aversive behavior and negative emotions (e.g., fear and sadness), and withdrawal in relation to the perceived stimulus. The latter had been observed in patients with depression [17–21] and comorbid anxiety [22,23] in multiple studies, and therefore recognized as a potential marker for depression [24]. The therapeutic value of inducing FAA in the brain of depressed patients, sometimes known as "alpha asymmetry training", has been demonstrated in multiple clinical studies [25–27]. We argue that passive environmental exposures, depending on their features, can induce either a pattern of brain activity associated with positive emotions and approach or the aversive pattern. Being able to identify urban settings and scenes inducing the FAA, and estimate the size of their therapeutic effect, can contribute to establishing new, cost-effective, widely accessible approaches to self-care and mental healthcare promotion. Such approaches have the potential to become a new self-care practice for diagnosed patients, and also of public health benefit in preventive care for urban dwellers at risk of mental health issues or who are looking for a mental health improvement regime.

1.2. Scope

Previous studies on the role of UGS on MH&WB have several limitations—including the lack of reliable physiological biomarkers and tools that can be deployed for an outdoor environment. For example, a relatively inexpensive and highly portable electroencephalography (EEG) apparatus, Emotiv EPOC has been used previously but its reliability is questionable due to high noise-sensitivity and generally poor performance [28]. Furthermore, previous studies did not attempt to establish causality between the actual exposure and MH&WB outcomes, but focused on correlational relationships [29–31].

In this study, we leveraged on the technological advances in neuroscience by using a non-invasive, portable yet reliable brain scanning equipment. We considered the passive exposure to the views as the most common and the most accessible type of interaction with the surrounding space. Additionally, in this preliminary phase we tested the passive exposures in situ, when immersed in actual outdoor spaces to ensure the ecological validity, rather than pictorial representations in the laboratory setting. The aim of the current study was to examine the effects of exposure to UGS with varying visual quality, on the pattern of brain activity recorded using EEG neuro-imaging. Data collection is ongoing. It is anticipated that the results of this study will provide novel information on the effects of the features of urban spaces on mood and will inform future intervention and prevention programs.

2. Materials and Methods

2.1. Participants

This is an on-going study and the results presented here are based on a sub-sample of 22 healthy volunteers (13 female, age M = 32.9, SD = 12.7) from Singapore. Participants were of Chinese (73%), Indian (5%) and other (22%) ethnicities. The full sample on completion will comprise n = 100. The inclusion criteria were: age between 21 and 75 years old, right-handed, no serious visual impairment, no pacemaker or recent otologic surgery and willing to commit to the full study period of three outdoor sessions. Participants were reimbursed with S$50 worth vouchers after completion of the sessions. One participant did not complete the experiment, without providing a reason, and therefore was not included in the analyzed sample. The study was granted NUS Ethical Committee's approval (ref#: S-18-352).

2.2. Sites and Scenes Selection

The selected sites are two UGS in Singapore (an urban park and a neighborhood green space), and one busy urban street (control) characterized by negligible greenery. Geographically, Singapore is located near the equator and has tropical climate with abundant rainfall (14 rainfall days per month), high and uniform temperatures and humidity all year round (28 °C, 70% Rh on average). Meteorological variables do not show large month to month variability and diurnal variations are strongly influenced by solar radiation [32].

Within each site, participants were exposed to three different landscape scenes with different landscape quality values and features within the view. Each of the scenes was previously annotated by four landscape architecture experts using the contemplative landscape model (CLM) and a mean was used to score each scene [33]. CLM is an expert-based instrument to assess level of aggregation of contemplative components of any given UGS within the viewing angle from the ground. There are seven key-components (and 36 possible subcomponents) of the CLM: landscape layers, landform, vegetation, color and light, compatibility, archetypal elements and character of peace and silence, each to be scored on a 1–6 Likert scale, which ranged from low to high aggregation level per component [33,34]. Higher scores were considered more contemplative. The most contemplative landscapes are considered to be soothing, restorative environments, which are inviting to rest, promote contact with nature, self-reflection and reorientation of one-self within a larger order [35,36]. Photographs of the selected scenes as well as their CL scores are presented in Figure 1.

2.3. Assessment of Participant's Depression

In order to control for depressive symptoms we utilized Beck Depression Inventory II (BDI), a 21-item self-reported multiple choice inventory, widely used as an indicator of severity of depression (81% of sensitivity and 92% specificity) [37].

Figure 1. Selected sites and scenes, with contemplative landscape score between 1 and 6 points for each scene.

2.4. Procedure

Data was collected between March and May 2019, during morning or late afternoon hours of the working week. Experimental sessions were scheduled individually, during one session there was one site with three scenes visited (order randomized [38]) Participants were blinded, to the hypothesis. Participants completed the self-reported Profile of Mood States questionnaire (POMS [39]) before and after each experimental session. Following that, they were seated on a chair facing the selected scene and EEG apparatus, V-amp 16-channel amplifier with dry active electrodes (Brain Products GmbH, Munich, Germany), was installed on their head. The participants were first instructed to put on the white mask blocking the view and then to relax, while equipment was calibrated and raw signal recording was initiated. After 1 min recording of the resting state with the mask on, the participants were asked to remove the mask and passively observe the landscape scene before them for another 1 min. Once this was completed, the 1 min resting state with mask on and 1 min scene watching was repeated for the same scene. This process was repeated for all the three scenes. Scenes locations as well as walking areas were selected in shaded areas to avoid excessive sun exposure. After the recording for all the three scenes were over, the participant completed the post- measurement POMS questionnaire. The duration of each session took between 30 and 45 min. Participants were allowed to drink water between the scenes but not to eat. Environmental variables (temperature, humidity, brightness and noise) were recorded with 4-in-1 environment meter (CEM, DT-8820) at each scene for each participant to control for confounding variables. The procedure on the day of testing is described in Figure 2.

Figure 2. Setup and procedure: (**a**) participant viewing the scene in S2_3, (**b**) participant during resting state in S3_1, (**c**) participant walking between the scenes in Site 1 and (**d**) steps of the in-situ experimental protocol.

2.5. EEG Data Processing

The EEG signal was processed offline using the Brain Analyzer 2 software (Brain Products GmbH, Munich, Germany). The raw signal had a 500 Hz sampling rate, with 2000 μS sampling interval, and was filtered with the high cutoff 40 Hz and 50 Hz notch filter. Channels were referenced according to the 10–20 international system and the visual inspection was performed to evaluate the signal quality, noisy or missing channels. Topographic interpolation of noisy or lost channels was performed where necessary, and ocular movements were corrected using the Independent Component Analysis (ICA) ocular correction function. Later, the 60 s long segments for both baseline and viewing conditions were extracted and non-complex fast Fourier transformation was performed on both segments. Further, the frequencies from two segments were averaged, and the alpha power (8–13 Hz) values for each electrode was extracted. The exported viewing data was then corrected for the baseline (viewing-baseline), and alpha power values for the left and right frontal regions were computed (Left = AFp1 + AFF5h + F7; Right = AFp2 + AFF6h + F8) [17,22]. Positive FAA values are indicative of more alpha power on the right frontal hemisphere as compared to left and negative of more alpha power on the left frontal hemisphere compared to the right. Higher values indicate higher FAA and are a marker of positive approach motivation as opposed to the withdrawal.

3. Statistical Analysis

A repeated measures general linear model (3 × 3) was used to test the main effect of site and the interaction between the site and the view on FAA. Unadjusted post-hoc comparisons were conducted to investigate specific group differences. In addition, to examine whether the landscape score (CLS) predicts FAA independently of the experimental condition, we used a linear regression model with bootstrapped 95% confidence intervals (CI), with 1000 samples and bias corrected accelerated CIs. For this purpose, CLS from the control condition were dummy coded and assigned a score of 1, while the raw CLS from the experimental conditions remained unchanged. As external conditions may impact the quality of exposure, data were re-analyzed after adjusting for Thom's discomfort index (TDI), which is a good summary measure of the external conditions [40]. Due to the small sample size it was not viable to control for additional environmental measures such as temperature or humidity. As the sensitivity analysis, all tests were repeated after adjusting for BDI and the results remained unchanged (not presented). Analyses were also adjusted for participant gender, and although the results did not change, there were some non-significant indications of potential gender differences in the responsiveness to the experimental manipulation (not reported here). Dependent subjects *t*-test was used to compare the before and after POMS scores. Analyses were conducted in IBM SPSS v.23 (IBM corp., Armonk, NY, USA) and the alpha level of 0.05 was used as an indicator of statistical significance.

4. Results

4.1. Sample Characteristics

Sample characteristics, including selected environmental metrics, are described in Table 1.

Table 1. Sample characteristics (mean, SD or #).

Variable	Participants in Preliminary Phase (*n* = 22)		
Age	M = 32.9 (SD = 12.7)		
Gender			
Male	9 (41%)		
Ethnicity			
Chinese	16 (73%)		
Indian	1 (5%)		
Others	5 (22%)		
Education			
Tertiary	20 (91%)		
Secondary	2 (9%)		
Profile of Nature Exposure [41]			
High (92%–100%)	0		
Versatile (70%–91%)	3 (14%)		
Unilateral (32%–69%)	19 (86%)		
Average (19%–31%)	0		
Low (0%–19%)	0		
Beck Depression Inventory-II			
Low (1–16 pt.)	19 (86%)		
Moderate (17–30 pt.)	3 (14%)		
Significant (31–>40 pt.)	0		
Inter-session break	M = 11 days (SD = 13 days)		
	Site 1	**Site 2**	**Site 3**
Temperature (°C)	M = 29.38 (SD = 0.63)	M = 27.73 (SD = 0.50)	M = 28.09 (SD = 0.62)
Humidity (%Rh)	M = 69.42 (SD = 0.62)	M = 72.13 (SD = 1.37)	M = 68.01 (SD = 0.30)
TDI	M = 26.76 (SD = 0.49)	M = 25.79 (SD = 0.41)	M = 26.52 (SD = 0.54)

Notes: Interpretation of TDI values—<21—no discomfort; 21–24—less than half population feels discomfort; 25–27—more than half population feels discomfort; 28–29—most population feels discomfort and deterioration of psychophysical conditions; 30–32—the whole population feels a heavy discomfort; >32—sanitary emergency due to the very strong discomfort, which may cause heatstroke.

4.2. Differences between the Sites and Views

Sphericity assumption was violated for the main effect and the interaction ($p < 0.05$), so multivariate tests (Pillai's trace) were reported alongside the within-subject effects, with degrees of freedom corrected using Greenhouse–Geisser estimates of sphericity.

The multivariate effects showed a non-significant trend for the main effect of site ($F_{(2, 15)} = 3.04$, $p = 0.078$), which was attenuated in the within-subjects tests ($F_{(1.17, 18.77)} = 1.37$, $p = 0.26$). After adjusting for TDI, the multivariate tests showed a significant main effect of site ($F_{(2,12)} = 5.14$, $p = 0.024$), which was slightly attenuated in the within-subjects tests ($F(1.15, 14.95 = 3.25, p = 0.087)$).

The highest mean FAA were recorded in Site 1 (urban park), and the lowest in Site 3 (urban street) and these are depicted in Figure 3a. Site 1 did not differ from Site 2 (neighborhood green space; $p = 0.61$) or Site 3 ($p = 0.20$), but Site 2 was significantly different from Site 3 ($p = 0.023$).

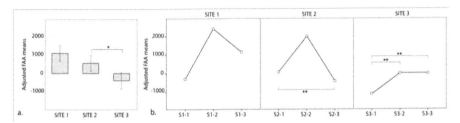

Figure 3. Differences in mean values of frontal alpha asymmetry (FAA) across participants passively viewing the landscapes: (**a**) within 3 sites (Site 1—Urban Park, Site 2—Residential Green and Site 3—Control (Busy Downtown) and (**b**) exposed to nine different scenes of these sites (S1_1, S1_2, S1_3, S2_1, S2_2, S2_3, S3_1, S3_2 and S3_3; * $p < 0.05$; ** $p < 0.1$).

The multivariate tests showed a non-significant trend for the interaction between the site and the view (F(4, 13) = 2.57, $p = 0.088$), which was not present in the within-subjects tests (F(1.48, 23.63) = 0.36, $p = 0.64$). These trends were further attenuated after adjusting for TDI in multivariate tests (F(4,10) = 1.84, $p = 0.20$) and though within-subjects comparisons showed significant interaction between the site and the view (F(1.67, 21.69 = 5.42, $p = 0.016$). The mean FAA across the sites and the views are summarized in Figure 3b.

Independently of the site, there was a non-significant weak positive association between the CLS and FAA ($\beta = 0.10$, $p = 0.16$), and adjusting for TDI did not influence that association ($\beta = 0.10$, $p = 0.17$).

In addition, there were no POMS changes before and after the exposure in Site 1 ($p > 0.05$) and Site 2 (>0.05). However, the total mood disturbance seemed to increase from before to after the exposure in the control group (t = −2.0, $p = 0.06$).

5. Discussion

This study examined FAA among participants exposed to UGS varying in visual quality. The preliminary results presented here show non-significant trends suggesting that passive visual exposure to certain UGS might be linked with higher alpha power in the right frontal lobes as compared to the left, compared to exposure to other UGS views for example landscapes in the residential areas. Moreover, same participants showed reverse pattern of brain activity (more alpha on the left compared to right lobe) when exposed to the busy street environment in high-density downtown with negligible greenery. Importantly, there was a trend for a non-significant interaction between the site and the view type, suggesting that even within the individual sites, there may be a heterogeneous response to different views and some scenes may induce more or less FAA response than others (Figure 3b). This finding informed a post-hoc hypothesis that, independently of the site, views with higher CLS might invoke higher FAA. We subsequently tested this assumption and the results showed a non-significant positive trend between CLS and FAA, suggesting that even within the residential areas, views with higher CLS might be beneficial for FAA, which might provide important information when planning the landscapes of residential areas in the future. After adjusting for environmental conditions, we observed stronger effects, which suggests that not controlling for the weather conditions, especially in countries with strong temperature and humidity variability might constitute a serious confounding factor in these types of experiments.

These preliminary findings support previous research findings suggesting that quality of green exposure can play a more important role than the quantity or accessibility of UGS for the MH&WB outcomes [29,42] and build on the previous research by providing evidence for an objective improvement in brain pattern activity typically associated with positive mood/affect. Nevertheless, this is the first study to demonstrate that in-situ exposure to a contemplative space can elicit FAA. Previous experimental studies on FAA were, to our best knowledge, conducted only in the indoor laboratory environment, and demonstrated greater FAA in the brain of healthy control as compared to depressed patients [17–24]. Studies also show that besides the withdrawal tendencies associated with depression,

FAA can be a marker of the positive and negative affects. For example, Davidson and colleagues [43], examined brainwaves of participants watching and evaluating television shows. Positively rated TV scenes were associated with greater relative left-hemispheric alpha frontal activation, while negatively rated scenes were associated with greater relative right-hemispheric frontal activation. Interestingly, previous within-subjects study on the brain response to contemplative landscape videos, conducted indoors, did not find FAA differences between contemplative and non-contemplative landscape exposure [44]. As for the previous experiments conducted outdoors, they did not examine the FAA patterns, but demonstrated that green urban spaces (often described as nature) triggered improved mood, emotional regulation, recovery from stress and mental fatigue as compared to exposure to space often defined as urban [45–47]. In our study we did not observe improved mood (as measured with POMS) between before and after the exposures in both green urban sites. However, we did observe decreased mood in the busy urban street site. This suggests that FAA may be a more accurate predictor of positive MH&WB outcomes caused by the urban landscape exposures, than the self-reported mood questionnaire such as POMS. Alternatively, it is plausible that these two measures capture different aspects of mood, which should be explored in future research. Moreover, the in-situ EEG measurement besides having more ecological validity, may also be more sensitive to differences in FAA, as compared to indoor lab exposures.

Future research will examine the differences in brain oscillations between indoor and outdoor exposure to contemplative and non-contemplative landscapes, including in the sample patients with diagnosed depression. We will also run the dose-response analysis, which will evaluate the optimal exposure time for the best MH&WB outcomes.

The strength of this study was a well-controlled experimental design with multiple conditions and objective physiological measures. The main limitation of the study was the small sample size at this preliminary stage, as the data collection was still ongoing. There also was a possibility of bias regarding the outlying FAA values, noticeable through the values of standard deviation varying between Site 1 and Site 2 and 3. However, the bias risk was mitigated by a within-subjects design, as each participant went through the same data collecting procedure in three different environments and to remain conservative all FAA values were adjusted for baseline.

6. Conclusions

On completion, the results of this study will provide a basis for prevention and interventions that target mental health outcomes and will be used as guidelines for designing UGS that are optimal for mental health promotion.

Author Contributions: Conceptualization, A.O.-G.; Methodology, A.O.-G.; Software, A.O.-G.; Validation, A.O.-G., R.H. and A.F.; Formal Analysis, A.O.-G., A.F.; Investigation, A.S.; Resources, A.S., R.H.; Data Curation, A.O.-G., A.F.; Writing—Original Draft Preparation, A.O.-G.; Writing—Review and Editing, A.S., R.H., A.F.; Visualization, A.O.-G.; Supervision, R.H.; Project Administration, R.H., A.S.; Funding Acquisition, A.S. All authors have read and agreed to the published version of the manuscript.

Funding: This research was funded by Ministry of National Development of Singapore, grant number R-722-000-010-490. And The article processing cost was funded by the indirect research grant provided by the National Parks Board and administered by the National University of Singapore (R-722-000-010-495).

Acknowledgments: We want to thank student assistants who helped with data collection, Radha Waykool, Manasi Prabhudesai, Estelle Mak and Rahul Verma, and all participants for their time and patience.

Conflicts of Interest: Authors declare no conflict of interest.

References

1. Helbich, M. Toward dynamic urban environmental exposure assessments in mental health research. *Environ. Res.* **2018**, *161*, 129–135. [CrossRef]

2. Helbich, M. Dynamic Urban Environmental Exposures on Depression and Suicide (NEEDS) in the Netherlands: A protocol for a cross-sectional smartphone tracking study and a longitudinal population register study. *BMJ Open* **2019**, *9*, e030075. [CrossRef] [PubMed]

3. Medina, J. Brain Rules. In *Brain Rules*; Pear Press: Seattle, WA, USA, 2018.

4. United Nations. *2018 Revision of the World Urbanization Prospects*; United Nations: Tokyo, Japan, 2018.

5. Beveridge, C.E.; Rocheleau, P. *Frederick Law Olmsted*; Rizzoli International Publications: New York, NY, USA, 1995.

6. Mueller, D.P. The current status of urban-rural differences in psychiatric disorder. An emerging trend for depression. *J. Nerv. Ment. Dis.* **1981**, *169*, 18–27. [CrossRef]

7. Peen, J.; Schoevers, R.A.; Beekman, A.T.; Dekker, J. The current status of urban-rural differences in psychiatric disorders. *Acta Psychiatr. Scand.* **2010**, *121*, 84–93. [CrossRef] [PubMed]

8. Berman, M.G.; Jonides, J.; Kaplan, S. The cognitive benefits of interacting with nature. *Psychol. Sci.* **2008**, *19*, 1207–1212. [CrossRef] [PubMed]

9. Kaplan, R.; Kaplan, S. *The Experience of Nature: A Psychological Perspective*; CUP: Cambridge, UK, 1989.

10. Hartig, T.; Staats, H. Guest's editors' introduction: Restorative environments. *J. Environ. Psychol.* **2003**, *23*, 103–107. [CrossRef]

11. Ulrich, R.S. Human responses to vegetation and landscapes. *Landsc. Urban Plan.* **1986**, *13*, 29–44. [CrossRef]

12. Kaplan, S. Meditation, Restoration, and the Management of Mental Fatigue. *Environ. Behav.* **2001**, *33*, 480–506. [CrossRef]

13. Hartig, T.; Staats, H. The need for psychological restoration as a determinant of environmental preferences. *J. Environ. Psychol.* **2006**, *26*, 215–226. [CrossRef]

14. Van den Berg, A.E.; Hartig, T.; Staats, H. Preference for Nature in Urbanized Societies: Stress, Restoration, and the Pursuit of Sustainability. *J. Soc. Issues* **2007**, *63*, 79–96. [CrossRef]

15. Hartig, T.; Mang, M.; Evans, G.W. Restorative effects of natural environment experiences. *Environ. Behav.* **1991**, *23*, 3–26. [CrossRef]

16. Ulrich, R. View through a window may influence recovery. *Science* **1984**, *224*, 224–225. [CrossRef] [PubMed]

17. Henriques, J.B.; Davidson, R.J. Left frontal hypoactivation in depression. *J. Abnorm. Psychol.* **1991**, *100*, 535. [CrossRef] [PubMed]

18. Bell, I.R.; Schwartz, G.E.; Hardin, E.E.; Baldwin, C.M.; Kline, J.P. Differential resting quantitative electroencephalographic alpha patterns in women with environmental chemical intolerance, depressives, and normals. *Biol. Psychiatry* **1998**, *43*, 376–388. [CrossRef]

19. Gotlib, I.H. EEG alpha asymmetry, depression, and cognitive functioning. *Cogn. Emot.* **1998**, *12*, 449–478. [CrossRef]

20. Debener, S.; Beauducel, A.; Nessler, D.; Brocke, B.; Heilemann, H.; Kayser, J. Is resting anterior EEG alpha asymmetry a trait marker for depression? *Neuropsychobiology* **2000**, *41*, 31–37. [CrossRef]

21. Pizzagalli, D.A.; Nitschke, J.B.; Oakes, T.R.; Hendrick, A.M.; Horras, K.A.; Larson, C.L.; Abercrombie, H.C.; Schaefer, S.M.; Koger, J.V.; Benca, R.M. Brain electrical tomography in depression: The importance of symptom severity, anxiety, and melancholic features. *Biol. Psychiatry* **2002**, *52*, 73–85. [CrossRef]

22. Sackeim, H.A.; Greenberg, M.S.; Weiman, A.L.; Gur, R.C.; Hungerbuhler, J.P.; Geschwind, N. Hemispheric asymmetry in the expression of positive and negative emotions: Neurologic evidence. *Arch. Neurol.* **1982**, *39*, 210–218. [CrossRef]

23. Banerjee, S.; Argaez, C. CADTH Rapid Response Reports. In *Neurofeedback and Biofeedback for Mood and Anxiety Disorders: A Review of Clinical Effectiveness and Guidelines*; Canadian Agency for Drugs and Technologies in Health: Ottawa, ON, Canada, 2017.

24. Harmon-Jones, E.; Allen, J.J. Behavioral activation sensitivity and resting frontal EEG asymmetry: Covariation of putative indicators related to risk for mood disorders. *J. Abnorm. Psychol.* **1997**, *106*, 159. [CrossRef]

25. Walker, J.; Lawson, R.; Kozlowski, G. Current status of QEEG and neurofeedback in the treatment of clinical depression. *Neurother. Cent. Dallas* **2006**, *343*, 1–21.

26. Rosenfeld, J.P. An EEG biofeedback protocol for affective disorders. *Clin. Electroencephalogr.* **2000**, *31*, 7–12. [CrossRef] [PubMed]

27. Baehr, E.; Rosenfeld, J.P.; Baehr, R. Clinical use of an alpha asymmetry neurofeedback protocol in the treatment of mood disorders: Follow-up study one to five years post therapy. *J. Neurother.* **2001**, *4*, 11–18. [CrossRef]

28. Duvinage, M.; Castermans, T.; Petieau, M.; Hoellinger, T.; Cheron, G.; Dutoit, T. Performance of the Emotiv Epoc headset for P300-based applications. *Biomed. Eng. Online* **2013**, *12*, 56. [CrossRef] [PubMed]
29. Gascon, M.; Triguero-Mas, M.; Martínez, D.; Dadvand, P.; Forns, J.; Plasència, A.; Nieuwenhuijsen, M.J. Mental health benefits of long-term exposure to residential green and blue spaces: A systematic review. *Int. J. Environ. Res. Public Health* **2015**, *12*, 4354–4379. [CrossRef]
30. Shanahan, D.F.; Bush, R.; Gaston, K.J.; Lin, B.B.; Dean, J.; Barber, E.; Fuller, R.A. Health Benefits from Nature Experiences Depend on Dose. *Sci. Rep.* **2016**, *6*, 28551. [CrossRef]
31. Van den Bosch, M. Live long in nature and long live nature! *Lancet Planet. Health* **2017**, *1*, e265–e266. [CrossRef]
32. Meteorological Service Singapore. Climate of Singapore. Available online: http://www.weather.gov.sg/climate-climate-of-singapore/ (accessed on 25 November 2019).
33. Olszewska, A.A.; Marques, P.F.; Ryan, R.L.; Barbosa, F. What makes a landscape contemplative? *Environ. Plan. B Urban Anal. City Sci.* **2016**, *45*, 7–25. [CrossRef]
34. Olszewska, A.A. Contemplative Values of Urban Parks and Gardens: Applying Neuroscience to Landscape Architecture. Ph.D. Thesis, Universidade do Porto, Porto, Portugal, 2016.
35. Treib, M. Attending. In *Contemporary Landscapes of Contemplation*; Routledge: Abingdon, UK, 2005; pp. 27–49.
36. Krinke, R. *Contemporary Landscapes of Contemplation*; Routledge: Abingdon, UK, 2005.
37. Beck, A.T.; Steer, R.A.; Brown, G.K. Beck depression inventory-II. *San Antonio* **1996**, *78*, 490–498.
38. Edwards, A.L. Balanced latin-square designs in psychological research. *Am. J. Psychol.* **1951**, *64*, 598–603. [CrossRef]
39. Shacham, S. A shortened version of the Profile of Mood States. *J. Personal. Assess.* **1983**, *47*, 305–306. [CrossRef]
40. Epstein, Y.; Moran, D.S. Thermal comfort and the heat stress indices. *Ind. Health* **2006**, *44*, 388–398. [CrossRef] [PubMed]
41. Hyvonen, K.; Tornroos, K.; Salonen, K.; Korpela, K.; Feldt, T.; Kinnunen, U. Profiles of Nature Exposure and Outdoor Activities Associated With Occupational Well-Being Among Employees. *Front. Psychol.* **2018**, *9*, 754. [CrossRef]
42. Fong, K.C.; Hart, J.E.; James, P. A Review of Epidemiologic Studies on Greenness and Health: Updated Literature Through 2017. *Curr. Environ. Health Rep.* **2018**, *5*, 77–87. [CrossRef] [PubMed]
43. Davidson, R.J.; Schwartz, G.E.; Saron, C.; Bennett, J.; Goleman, D.J. Frontal versus parietal EEG asymmetry during positive and negative affect. *Psychophysiology* 1979, 16, 202–203.
44. Olszewska-Guizzo, A.A.; Paiva, T.O.; Barbosa, F. Effects of 3D Contemplative Landscape Videos on Brain Activity in a Passive Exposure EEG Experiment. *Front. Psychiatry* **2018**, *9*, 317. [CrossRef]
45. Bornioli, A.; Parkhurst, G.; Morgan, P.L. The psychological wellbeing benefits of place engagement during walking in urban environments: A qualitative photo-elicitation study. *Health Place* **2018**, *53*, 228–236. [CrossRef]
46. Zhang, Y.; Liu, C.; Herrup, K.; Shi, B.E. Physiological Responses of the Youth Viewing a Japanese Garden. In Proceedings of 2018 40th Annual International Conference of the IEEE Engineering in Medicine and Biology Society (EMBC), Honolulu, HI, USA, 18–21 July 2018; pp. 1550–1553.
47. Triguero-Mas, M.; Gidlow, C.J.; Martínez, D.; De Bont, J.; Carrasco-Turigas, G.; Martínez-Íñiguez, T.; Hurst, G.; Masterson, D.; Donaire-Gonzalez, D.; Seto, E. The effect of randomised exposure to different types of natural outdoor environments compared to exposure to an urban environment on people with indications of psychological distress in Catalonia. *PLoS ONE* **2017**, *12*, e0172200. [CrossRef]

MDPI

St. Alban-Anlage 66

4052 Basel

Switzerland

Tel. +41 61 683 77 34

Fax +41 61 302 89 18

www.mdpi.com

International Journal of Environmental Research and Public Health Editorial Office

E-mail: ijerph@mdpi.com

www.mdpi.com/journal/ijerph

Printed in the USA
CPSIA information can be obtained
at www.ICGtesting.com
LVHW071223081123
763392LV00010B/45